First published in the UK by Scholastic, 2021
Euston House, 24 Eversholt Street, London, NW1 1DB
Scholastic Ireland, 89E Lagan Road, Dublin Industrial Estate,
Glasnevin, Dublin, D11 HP5F

SCHOLASTIC and associated logos are trademarks and/or
registered trademarks of Scholastic Inc.

First published in the US by The Pokémon Company International, 2015

©2021 Pokémon. ©1995–2021 Nintendo / Creatures Inc. / GAME FREAK inc. TM, ®, and character
names are trademarks of Nintendo.

Copyright ©2021 The Pokémon Company International

ISBN 978 0702 31335 6

A CIP catalogue record for this book is available from the British Library.

Printed and bound in China
Paper made from wood grown in sustainable forests and
other controlled sources.

2 4 6 8 10 9 7 5 3 1

The publisher does not have any control over and does not assume any
responsibility for author or third-party websites or their content.

www.scholastic.co.uk

How this book works

The paper templates used to fold the characters from are found on pages 49 to 80. Since this is a book for ordinary people, not Origami Masters with five hands and extra long fingers, the designs have been kept as simple as possible by sometimes using two or more sheets of paper.

The projects are arranged so that the easiest characters to fold are at the beginning and the most difficult are at the end. You can jump straight into folding Eevee if you like, but it might be better to fold Munchlax first and fold Eevee once you have gained a little bit of experience and skill.

Each project tells you which template you should use to make the character. There is an asterisk on the back of each template that tells you which way up the paper should be when you begin to fold. Then it's just a matter of following the folding instructions.

Occasionally you will need to make cuts or use tape or glue when you see the scissor, tape, or glue symbols.

How to understand the folding instructions

Origami folding instructions show you in pictures, and tell you in words, how to fold the paper step by step to create your Pokémon characters. Here's how it works:

Let's begin with a simple sequence of 3 pictures and written explanations that show you how to make just one simple fold.

 **1** Fold in half sideways.

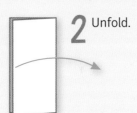 **2** Unfold.

 **3** Finished.

Here are the things you need to know to be able to follow simple diagrams like this:

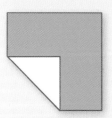

The edges of the paper are shown as solid lines. The front of the paper is shown shaded and the back of the paper is shown white. It's important to check before and after every fold that your paper looks the same as the pictures.

Picture 1 is a folding instruction made up of two parts, a movement arrow and a fold line. The movement arrow tells you which part of the paper moves, which direction it moves in and where it ends up. In this case, the movement arrow tells you to pick up the right edge of the paper and fold it across to the left in front until it lies on top of the left edge. The two edges of the paper are the location points for this fold, i.e. the points (usually either edges, corners or creases) that you use to help you make the fold accurately.

Key to symbols

 This push arrow symbol tells you that you need to turn a corner or a point inside out.

 This symbol tells you to turn the paper over, usually sideways.

 This symbol tells you that the next diagram has been drawn on a larger scale.

 A circle is used to highlight particular areas mentioned in the instruction.

 You will need to use glue where you see this symbol.

 You will need to use scissors where you see this symbol.

 You will need to use tape where you see this symbol.

When you have made a fold you will need to flatten it to make a crease. The fold line shows you where this crease will form. It's always a good idea to flatten the paper completely, press it down firmly with the soft part of a finger, then run a nail along the edge to make your crease really sharp. Once you have flattened a fold to create a sharp crease you will have created a line of permanent weakness in the paper.

Picture 2 shows you what the result of making the first fold will look like. Sometimes edges that lie exactly on top of each other as the result of a fold are shown slightly offset on the "after" diagram so that you can see they are there. Sometimes this isn't necessary and only the front edge is shown. Try not to let this confuse you.

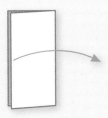

Sometimes a movement arrow is used without a fold line to mean open out using the crease you have already made. Every picture in a folding sequence (apart from the first and the last) is both an "after" picture for the step before and a "before" picture for the step after. So step 2 shows you the result of following the folding instruction contained in step 1, but also gives you another instruction that leads to step 3.

In the third picture the crease you made in step 1 is shown as a thin line. The trick to following folding instructions is to always look one step ahead so that you know what the result of making a fold should look like before you begin to make it.

Here are a few more things you need to know about the folding instructions and how they work.

This version of the movement arrow means fold, crease firmly, then unfold. This picture is a combination of instructions 1 and 2 and is a kind of shorthand used to save space in the book.

A dashed and dotted fold line with a dotted movement arrow means that the fold should be made away from you behind the paper. So this folding instruction means fold the right edge backward behind the paper onto the back of the left edge, then flatten to a crease.

A picture of this kind tells you to swivel the white triangular flap to the back by reversing the direction of the existing crease. The crease acts like a hinge when you do this.

Sometimes the two different types of fold line are used together to show you how a combination of creases made in different directions through the paper (some backward, some forward) can be used to collapse the paper into a different shape.

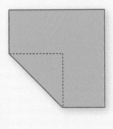

Dotted lines are also occasionally used to show hidden edges or fold lines, imaginary lines that are used to help locate a fold or lines to cut along. Sometimes they are also used to show where the paper will end up after you have made a fold. This picture shows what the result of following the folding instruction above would look like.

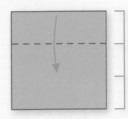

This type of symbol shows that the edge of the paper should be imagined as divided into a number of equal sections to help you locate a fold. In this case you would fold the top edge downward to make a crease one third of the way down the paper. It is normally OK for this division to be approximate rather than accurate.

Pikachu

With a brave heart and incredible lightning speed, Pikachu is the Pokémon ready to tackle any challenge! And with a twisty Thunderbolt tail and rounded cheeks and head, this origami Pokémon is worth a few more folds. Give it your all when you fold this one and see a familiar face look back at you in thanks!

TYPE: Electric **HEIGHT:** 0.4 m/1'04" **WEIGHT:** 6.0 kg/13.2 lbs

How To Make
Pikachu

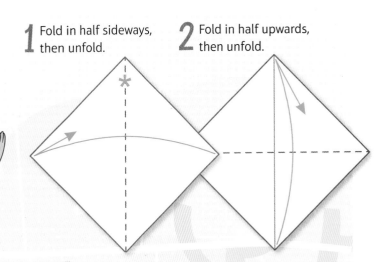

Pikachu is folded from a single square of paper. Part of the paper is cut off in step 13 to become the tail.

The template for Pikachu is on page 49. Make sure you start folding with the plain side of the paper facing towards you and with the asterisk at the top.

1 Fold in half sideways, then unfold.

2 Fold in half upwards, then unfold.

3 Fold two of the edges into the centre like this, then unfold.

4 Fold the other two edges into the centre in the same way (but don't unfold this time).

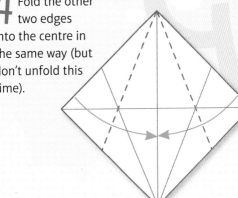

5 Fold the top point onto the bottom point, then unfold.

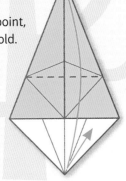

6 Fold the bottom section of the right-hand top layer upwards using the crease you made in step 5 and flatten the paper to look like picture 7.

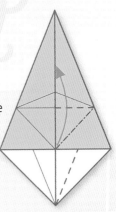

7 Repeat step 6 on the left-hand half of the paper.

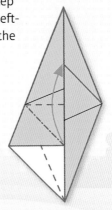

8 Fold the lower left edge inwards so that it passes through the corner marked with a circle. Picture 9 shows what the result should look like.

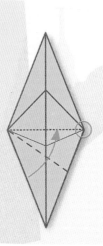

9 Unfold.

10 Repeat step 8 in the opposite direction.

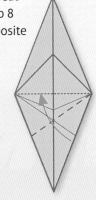

11 Fold the top layer across to the right so that it flattens to look like picture 12.

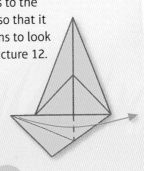

12 Fold the new point across to the left, crease firmly, then stand up at right angles to the rest of the paper.

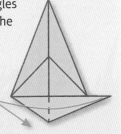

13 Cut carefully along the dotted line to remove the point that is sticking up. This will become Pikachu's tail.

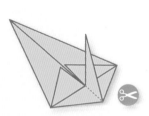

14 Fold both small central flaps downwards.

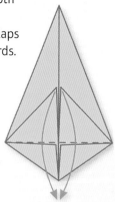

15 Fold both outside corners into the centre.

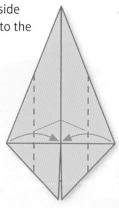

16 Turn over sideways.

Turn o

17 Fold the top point downwards so that the top left corner ends up lying on the left end of the crease made in step 2 (both marked with circles).

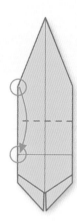

18 Fold the new bottom point upwards like this. The crease should be made approximately one third of the way down the right edge of the top layer.

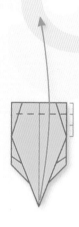

19 Turn both bottom corners of the front layer inside out between the other layers.

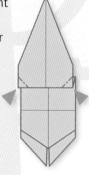

20 This is what the result should look like. Turn over sideways.

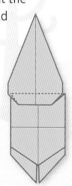

Turn over

21 Fold both top corners of the front layer inwards like this.

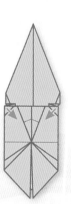

22 Fold the top point downwards to the position shown in picture 23. Make two tiny folds to make the ends of the feet blunt.

23 Cut along the crease marked with a dotted line to separate the ears. Fold the feet upwards as shown.

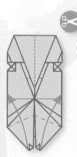

24 Make two tiny folds to round off the top of the head. Fold the bottom point upwards as shown and crease firmly.

25 Fold the ears upwards and outwards so that they look like picture 26. Fold the bottom left and right corners inwards to line up with the layers of paper behind them.

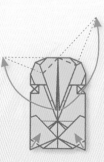

26 Fold the feet downwards as far as they will go.

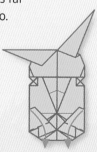

27 Turn over sideways.

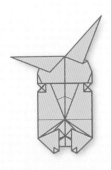

Turn over

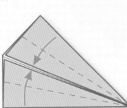

28 Push the paper between the feet backwards and upwards. You will be able to feel where to make this fold. You may need to fold the whole model in half backwards in order to crease this fold. If you do this, be careful not to split the front layers of the paper.

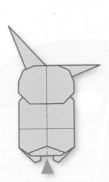

29 Pikachu's body is finished.

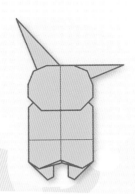

Folding and attaching the tail

30 Open out the piece of paper you cut off in step 13. Fold both the long outside edges into the centre.

31 Fold in half downwards.

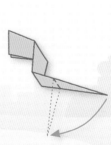

32 Fold the right point of the tail downwards so that it ends up in the position marked by the dotted lines.

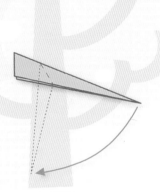

33 Fold the bottom point across to the right so that it ends up in the position marked by the dotted lines.

34 Fold the right point of the tail downwards so that it ends up in the position marked by the dotted lines.

35 Fold the bottom point across to the right so that it ends up in the position marked by the dotted lines.

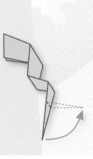

36 The tail is finished.

37 Attach the tail with a small piece of tape like this.

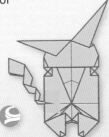

38 Pikachu is finished. You've created an awesome origami Pokémon!

Turn over

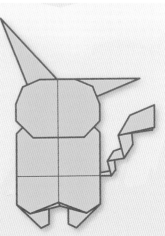

Munchlax

Munchlax is a relaxed sort of Pokémon and always hungry. Well, that makes for a nice round belly and a chilled attitude. Give Munchlax some rounded, mellow folds and see how it works out. It doesn't get stressed out!

TYPE: Normal **HEIGHT:** 0.6 m/2'00" **WEIGHT:** z105.0 kg/231.5 lbs

How To Make
Munchlax

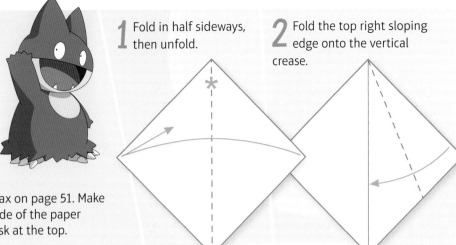

Munchlax is folded from a single square of paper. Although this design looks simple it contains two quite challenging moves (steps 10, 11 and 15).

You can find the template for Munchlax on page 51. Make sure you start folding with the white side of the paper facing towards you and with the asterisk at the top.

1 Fold in half sideways, then unfold.

2 Fold the top right sloping edge onto the vertical crease.

3 Repeat step 2 on the other half of the paper.

4 Turn over sideways.

Turn over

5 Fold in half downwards, then unfold.

6 This is what it should look like. Turn over sideways.

Turn over

7 Fold the bottom point upwards like this.

8 Fold in half downwards.

9 Swing the top edge backwards using the crease you made in step 5. Allow the front layers to swing upwards as you do this.

10 Separate the two sides of the back layers and gently pull out the right-hand side upwards and to the right. You will be able to flatten it to look like picture 11.

11 Repeat step 10 on the left-hand side of the design.

12 This is what the paper should look like now. Turn over sideways.

Turn over

13 Fold the bottom corners of the top layers inwards and upwards like this.

14 Unfold.

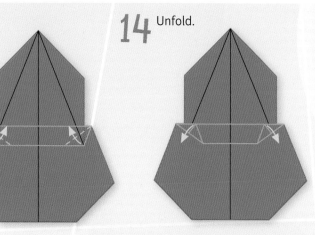

15 Very gently and carefully turn these two corners inside out between the back and front layers by reversing the direction of the crease you made in step 13. Be careful not to tear the paper as you do this.

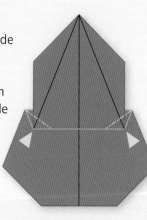

16 Fold the front layers in half downwards.

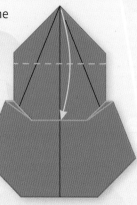

17 Swing the front layers out of sight behind by reversing the direction of the crease made in step 16.

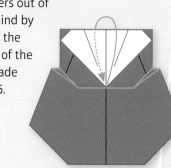

18 Turn over sideways.

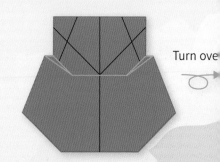

Turn over

19 Separate the two sides of the front layers at the top by cutting along the dotted line. Also fold the front layer at the bottom in half downwards, then unfold.

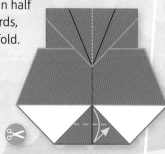

20 Fold both top corners inwards like this. Also fold the bottom edge upwards onto the crease you made in step 19.

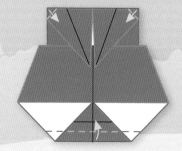

21 Fold the ears upwards like this. Try to end up with the creases in the middle of the ears vertical. See picture 22.

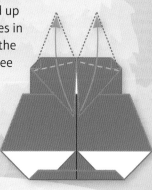

22 Fold both outside edges inwards as far as they will go, making sure the new creases are parallel to the edges.

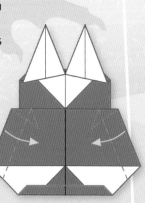

23 Turn over sideways.

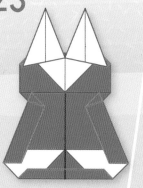

24 Fold the two halves of the design slightly backwards along the line of the vertical crease. This will help to keep the layers together. Munchlax is finished.

Turn over

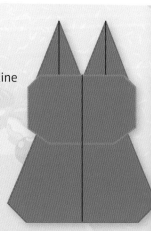

Fennekin

The fiery big-eared Fennekin brings quick wits and foxy magic to everyday life. This origami version keeps the ears and the colour – you give it a bit of attitude! Keep this one crisp and you'll be rewarded with a Pokémon that looks good anywhere.

TYPE: Fire **HEIGHT:** 0.4 m/1'04" **WEIGHT:** 9.4 kg/20.7 lbs

How To Make
Fennekin

Fennekin is folded from three sheets of paper – a full-size square, which becomes the head, and two quarter-size squares, which become the body and the tail. You can find the templates on page 53.

Folding the body

Make sure you start folding the quarter size square with the white side of the paper facing towards you and with the asterisk at the top.

1 Fold in half downwards.

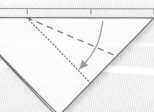

2 Fold the right corner inwards like this. Note that the crease begins about two thirds of the way along the top edge and that the moving edge ends up parallel to the left sloping edge.

3 Fold the bottom point of the front layer inwards like this. Also fold the top left point inwards as shown.

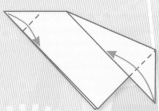

4 Fold the front layer backwards so that it ends up in between the other layers by reversing the direction of the crease you made in step 3.

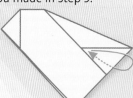

5 Fold the right-hand sloping edge inwards to create the neck like this.

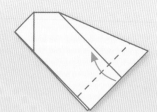

6 Fennekin's body is finished.

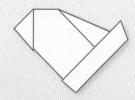

Folding the tail

Make sure you start folding the quarter size square with the white side of the paper facing towards you and with the asterisk at the top.

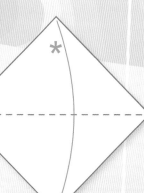

7 Fold in half downwards.

8 Fold both outside corners onto the bottom point.

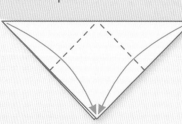

9 This is the result. The next picture is on a larger scale.

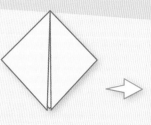

10 Fold both outside corners inwards like this. These folds are the same as the fold made in step 2.

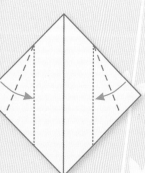

11 Fold both outside corners inwards again like this.

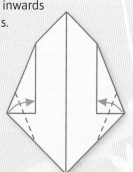

12 Fennekin's tail is finished.

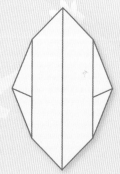

Folding the head

Make sure you start folding the full-size square with the white side of the paper facing towards you and with the asterisk at the top.

13 Fold in half sideways, then unfold.

14 Fold in half downwards.

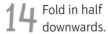
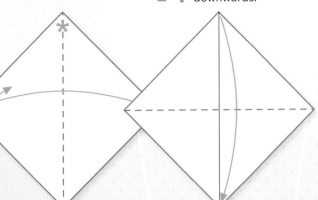

15 Fold both sloping edges onto the vertical crease.

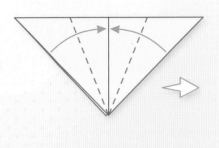

16 Fold the top points in half downwards.

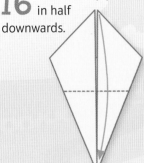

17 Fold the front layer in half downwards, allowing the back layers to flip upwards as you make the fold.

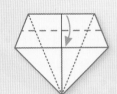

18 Fold the bottom right corner of the front layers inwards like this.

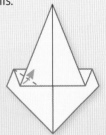

19 Unfold.

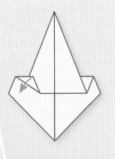

20 Now turn this corner inside out between the other layers by reversing the direction of the crease made in step 18.

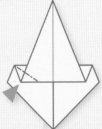

21 Turn over sideways.

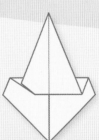

22 Make a small cut in the front layers along the vertical dotted line.

Turn over

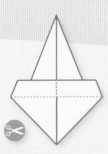

23 Pull the front left-hand layer out in the direction of the arrow.

24 Fold the left-hand flap across to the right so that it ends up in the position marked by the dotted lines.

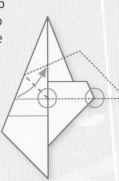

25 Fold the top flap back across to the left so that it ends up in the position marked by the dotted lines.

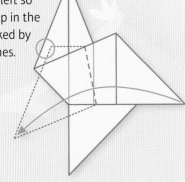

26 Fold the top point downwards so that the left edge just touches the top right corner of the front layer. Also fold the right edge of the middle layers inwards as far as it will go.

27 Flatten the layers firmly at the point marked with a circle. Fold the top front layer upwards as shown to form Fennekin's nose. Also fold the top left corner of the middle layers inwards as shown to shape Fennekin's ear.

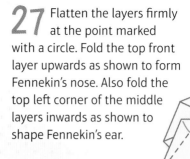

28 Make this tiny fold to start shaping the face.

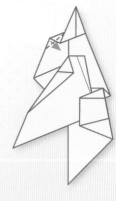

29 Finish shaping the face by folding the left edge of the back layers inwards like this.

30 This is the result. Turn over sideways and rotate to look like picture 31.

31 Fennekin's head is finished.

Turn over

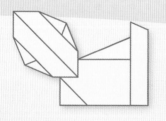

Putting Fennekin together

32 Apply a little glue to Fennekin's body at the point marked with a circle and attach the tail.

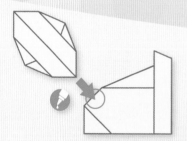

33 Turn over sideways.

Turn over

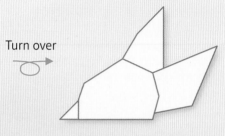

34 Apply a little glue to Fennekin's neck at the point marked with a circle and attach the head.

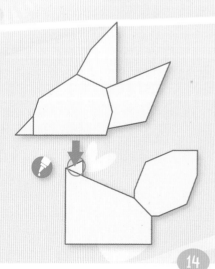

35 Fennekin is finished.

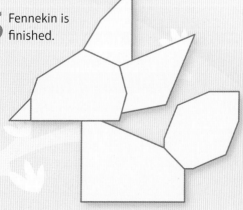

Scraggy

Scraggy is a tough, rough and sometimes ragged Pokémon. Here's a chance to fold mean and fold clean at the same time. Can you make your Scraggy look rough and tough?

TYPE: Dark-Fighting **HEIGHT:** 0.6 m/2'00" **WEIGHT:** 11.8 kg/26.0 lbs

How To Make
Scraggy

Scraggy is folded from three sheets of paper – a full-size square, which becomes the body and legs, and two quarter-size squares, which become the head and the tail.
  You can find the templates on page 55.

Folding the body and legs
Make sure you start folding the full-size square with the decorated side of the paper facing towards you and with the asterisk at the top. The asterisk is printed on the white side of the paper.

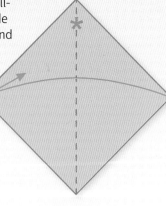

1 Fold in half sideways, then unfold.

2 Fold in half upwards, then unfold.

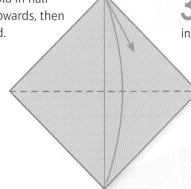

3 Fold both outside corners into the centre.

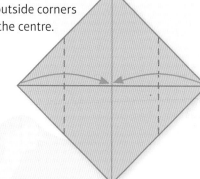

4 Turn over sideways.

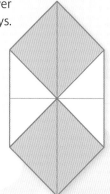

Turn over

5 Fold both outside edges into the centre, allowing the layers at the back to swivel into view.

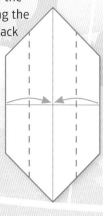

6 Fold the bottom point into the centre. Also fold the top left corner inwards as shown.

7 Fold the top right corner inwards in exactly the same way.

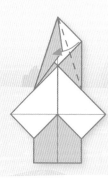

8 Fold the top point down to the bottom.

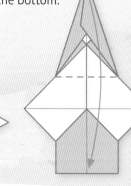

9 Fold the front point upwards so that the new crease lies on top of the existing horizontal crease.

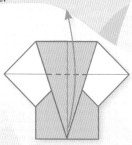

10 Separate the legs by cutting along the dotted line. This cut is made in the front layers only.

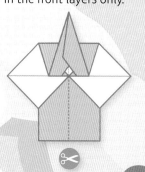

11 Fold the right leg downwards like this, making sure that the right edge of the leg is vertical.

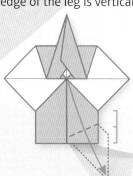

12 The result should look like this. Repeat step 11 to fold the left leg downwards.

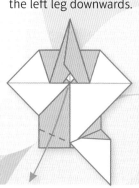

13 Shape the body by folding both outside corners inwards like this. Also shape the legs by folding the top corners inwards as far as they will go. Picture 14 shows what this should look like.

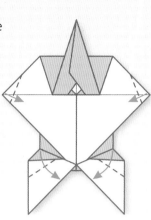

14 The circles mark the corners of the back layer of paper. Fold the shoulders and the bottom points inwards as shown to finish shaping the body and the feet.

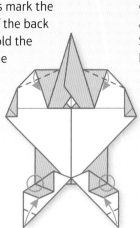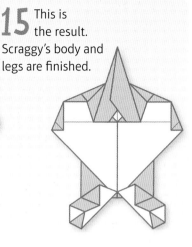

15 This is the result. Scraggy's body and legs are finished.

Folding the head

Make sure you start folding the quarter-size square with the white side of the paper facing towards you and with the asterisk at the top.

16 Fold in half sideways, then unfold.

17 Fold in half upwards, then unfold.

18 Fold both the top and bottom corners into the centre.

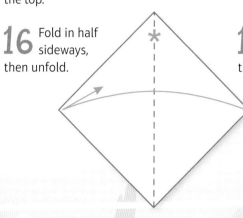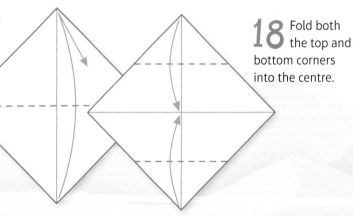

19 Fold the top front flap upwards like this.

20 Fold both the left and right corners inwards to the quarter way points. You don't need to do this completely accurately.

21 Turn over sideways. Scraggy's head is finished.

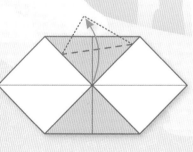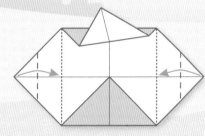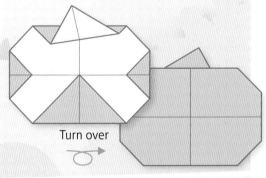

Turn over

Folding the tail

Make sure you start folding the quarter-size square with the white side of the paper facing towards you.

22 Fold in half downwards, then unfold.

23 Fold both the top and bottom left-hand sloping edges onto the horizontal crease.

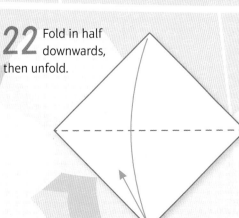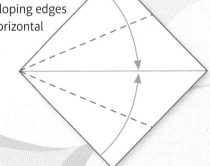

24 Fold in half downwards.

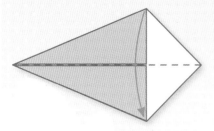

25 Fold the left point downwards like this, making sure that the crease starts from the position marked with a circle.

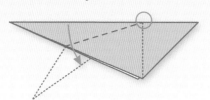

26 Fold the left point upwards again like this.

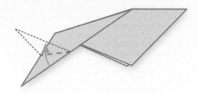

27 Fold the tip of the left point downwards again. Turn over sideways.

28 Fold the new left point inwards like this. Turn over sideways.

Turn over

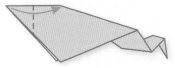

29 Scraggy's tail is finished and ready to be attached to its body.

Turn over

Putting Scraggy together

30 The flap created in step 28 goes inside the slit in the centre. The bottom of the tail tucks inside the layers at the top of the left leg.

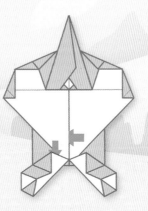

31 The result should look like this. The tail is now loosely attached to the body. You can glue it in place if you want it attached more firmly. Turn over sideways.

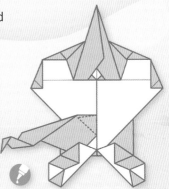

Turn over

32 Apply a little glue to the top of the neck and attach the head.

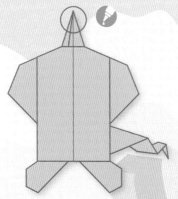

33 Scraggy is finished.

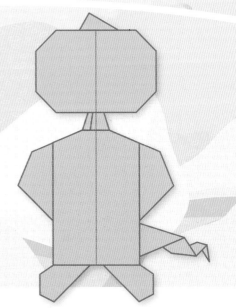

Bulbasaur

Origami has long been known for some simple shapes, like an origami frog. This Bulbasaur updates that traditionally folded figure for something a bit more modern: the very first Pokémon in the Pokédex, the Seed Pokémon Bulbasaur. Grow your folding skills!

TYPE: Grass-Poison **HEIGHT:** 0.7 m/2'04" **WEIGHT:** 6.9 kg/15.2 lbs

How To Make
Bulbasaur

Bulbasaur is folded from a single square of paper. You need to have acquired a little bit of experience and skill by folding easier designs before you attempt this one.

You can find the template for Bulbasaur on page 57. Make sure you start folding with the white side of the paper facing towards you and with the asterisk at the top.

1 Fold in half downwards.

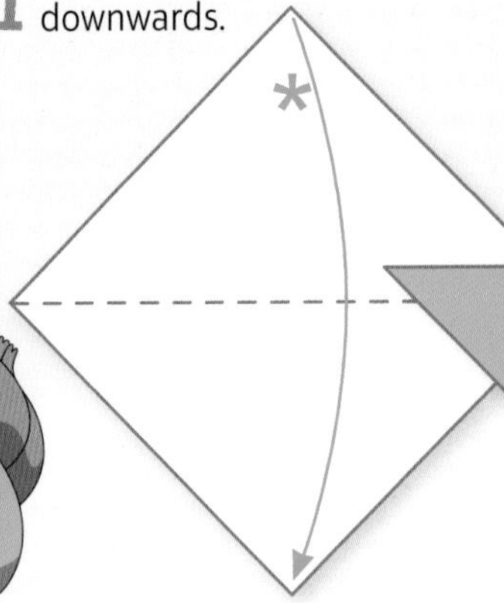

2 Fold the right corner onto the bottom corner.

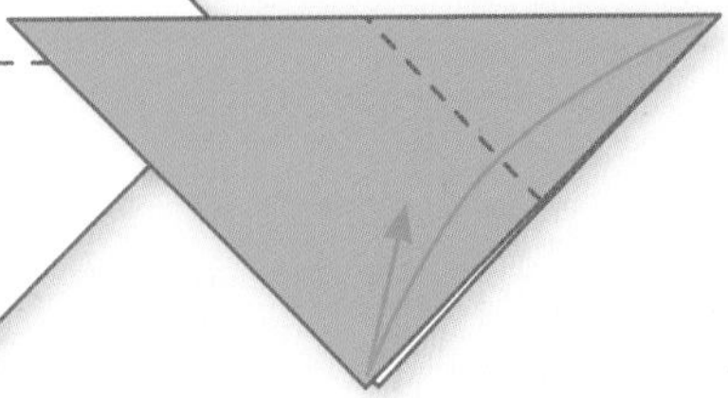

3 Fold the left edge of the front layer onto the top right sloping edge.

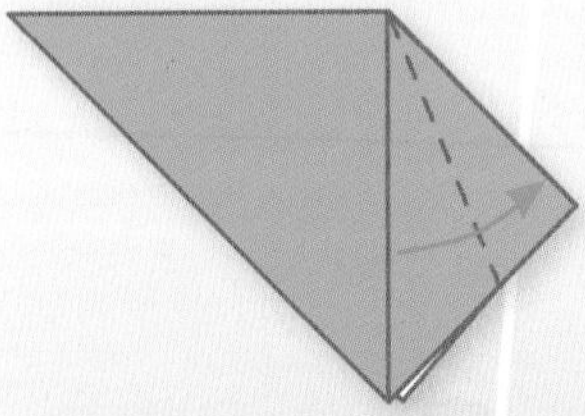

4 Undo the last two folds by pulling the top layers out like this.

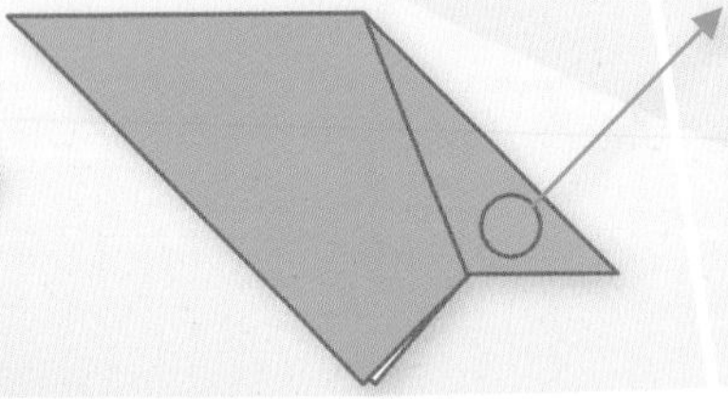

5 Lift up the right corner and flatten to look like picture 6.

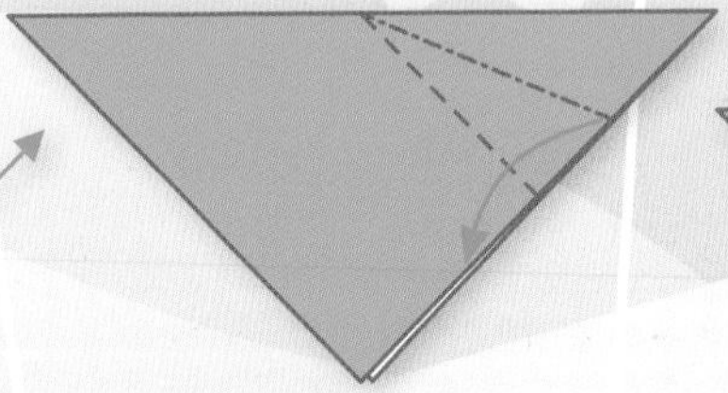

6 Turn over sideways and rotate to look like picture 7.

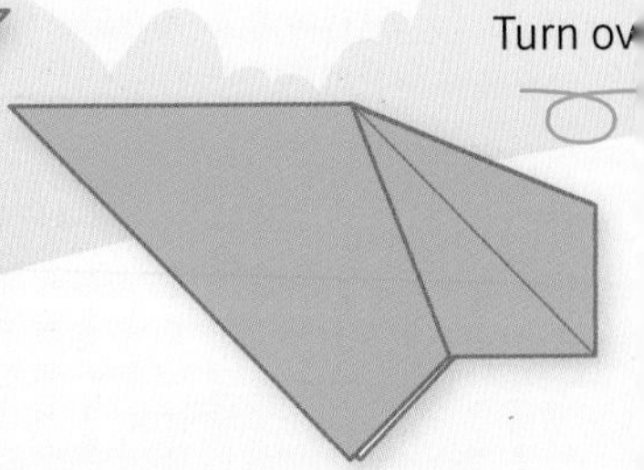

Turn ov

7 Fold the left point onto the other end of the horizontal crease. Try to make sure the layers do not separate as you do this.

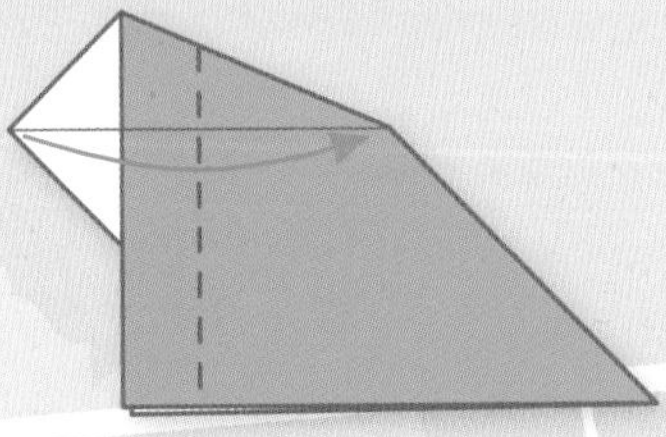

8 Turn over sideways.

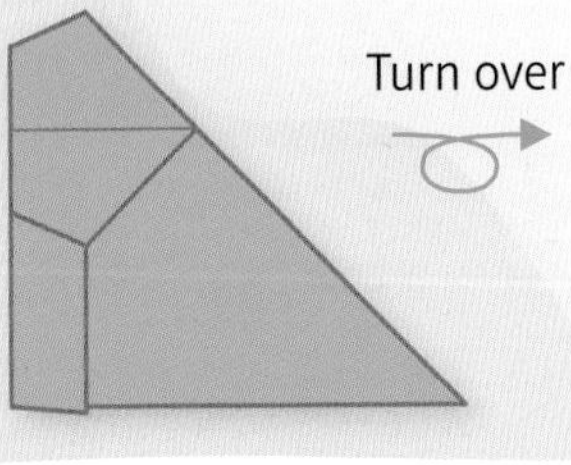

Turn over

9 Fold the left point across to the right so that the top edge of the new front layer is at right angles to the vertical edge. The set square shows where this should happen. The next picture is on a larger scale.

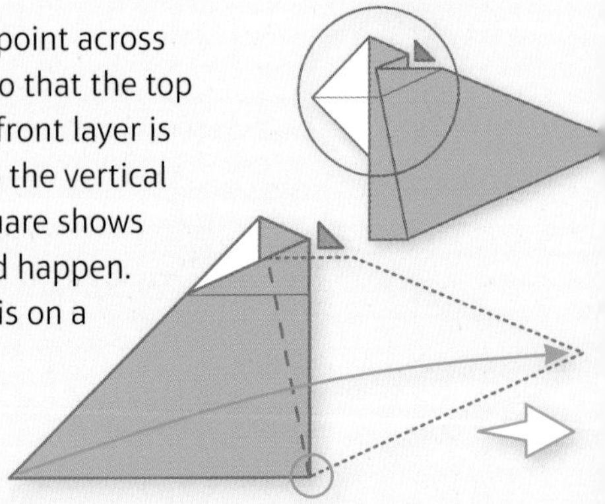

10 Fold the left corner inwards as shown.

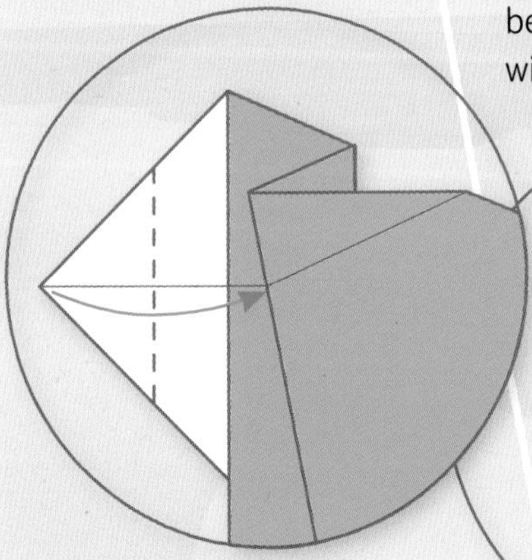

11 Fold the top corner inwards as shown. Also tuck the front layer into the pocket behind it at the point marked with a circle.

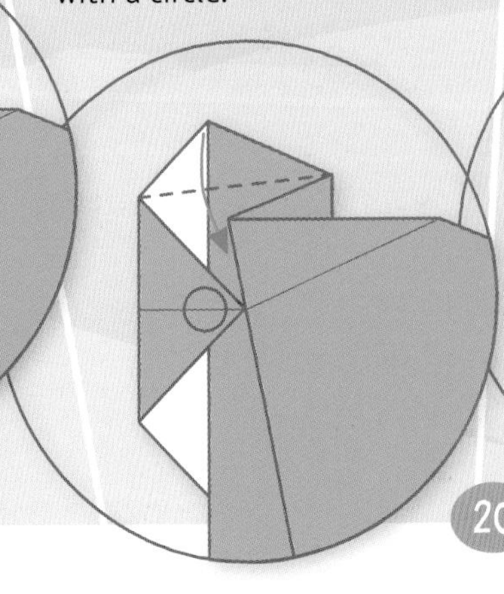

12 Fold both top corners inwards like this.

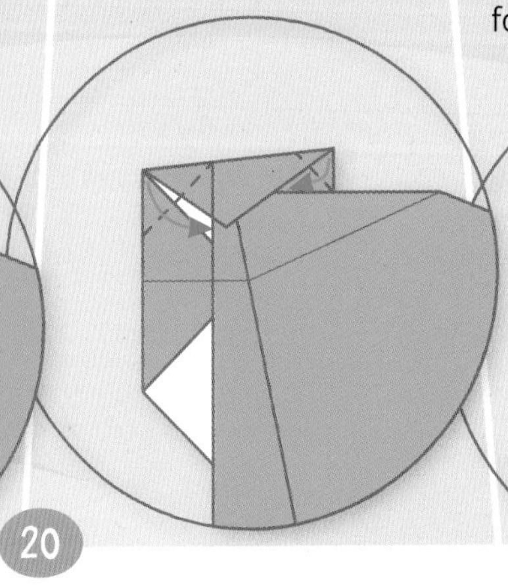

13 Unfold the top right corner. Also fold the front layer at the top left corner outwards again to form one of Bulbasaur's ears.

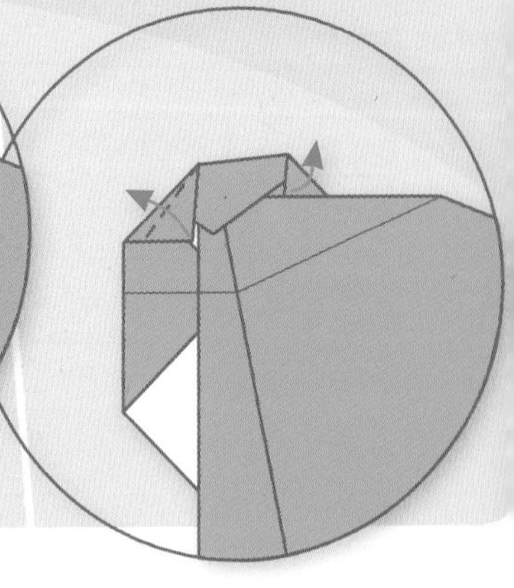

14 Tuck the flap marked with a circle underneath the layers of paper behind it.

15 Turn the top right corner inside out between the other layers using the existing creases.

16 The result should look like this.

17 Pull the right point downwards to undo the folds made in steps 9 and 15.

18 Fold the bottom of the front layers upwards using the existing crease.

19 Cut along the dotted line. This cut is very short. It should be just long enough to enable you to fold this corner inwards (see step 21) to match the size of the corner you folded inwards in step 13.

20 This is how small the cut should be. Repeat folds 11, 12 and the second part of fold 13 to shape the other half of Bulbasaur's head.

21 The result should look like this. Undo fold 18.

22 Fold the right point across to the left so that the crease forms in the position shown. Look at picture 23 (which is on a larger scale) to see what the result should look like.

23 The upper circle is there to show you that the sloping edge of the front layer should lie parallel to the crease just above it. Turn over sideways and rotate to look like picture 24.

24 Fold the top right corner diagonally inwards like this. The location points for this fold are marked with circles. Undo the fold.

Turn over

25 Fold the right edge onto the bottom edge.

26 Fold the right side of the paper backwards like this. Note that the top of the fold should ideally be at the same height as the top of the head.

27 Open out the fold you made in step 26. Undo the fold you made in step 25.

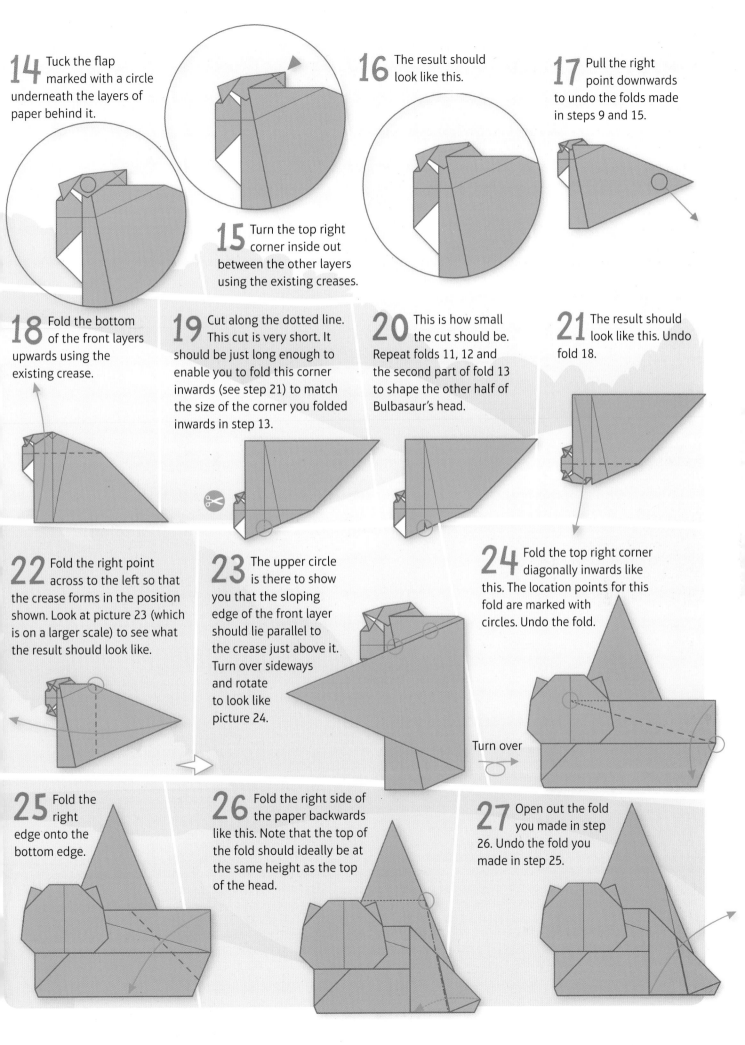

28 Remake the fold you made in step 24 using the same crease. Remake the fold you made in step 26 through all the layers of the paper, then unfold.

29 Undo the first fold you made in step 28. Remake the fold you made in step 25.

30 Tuck point x diagonally downwards underneath the front layers using the crease you made in step 28. Look at picture 31 to see what the result should look like.

31 The position of the hidden layers of paper is shown by the dotted lines. Fold the left edge of the front layer backwards inside the design to create Bulbasaur's back leg.

32 Make three small cuts in the bottom edge along the dotted lines in the way shown here.

33 Fold the second to right-hand section of the bottom edge upwards to create space between the front and back legs. Also make two tiny backwards folds to separate the front legs. Turn over sideways.

Turn

34 Fold the bottom left corner inwards like this. Also make the fold on the right-hand side of the design using the existing crease and flatten to look like picture 35.

35 Fold the left edge inwards using the existing crease.

36 Fold the top point diagonally downwards like this. The location points for this fold are marked with circles.

37 Fold the left point of the front layer across to the right like this.

38 Fold the top point downwards like this.

39 Turn over sideways.

Turn over

40 Bulbasaur is finished.

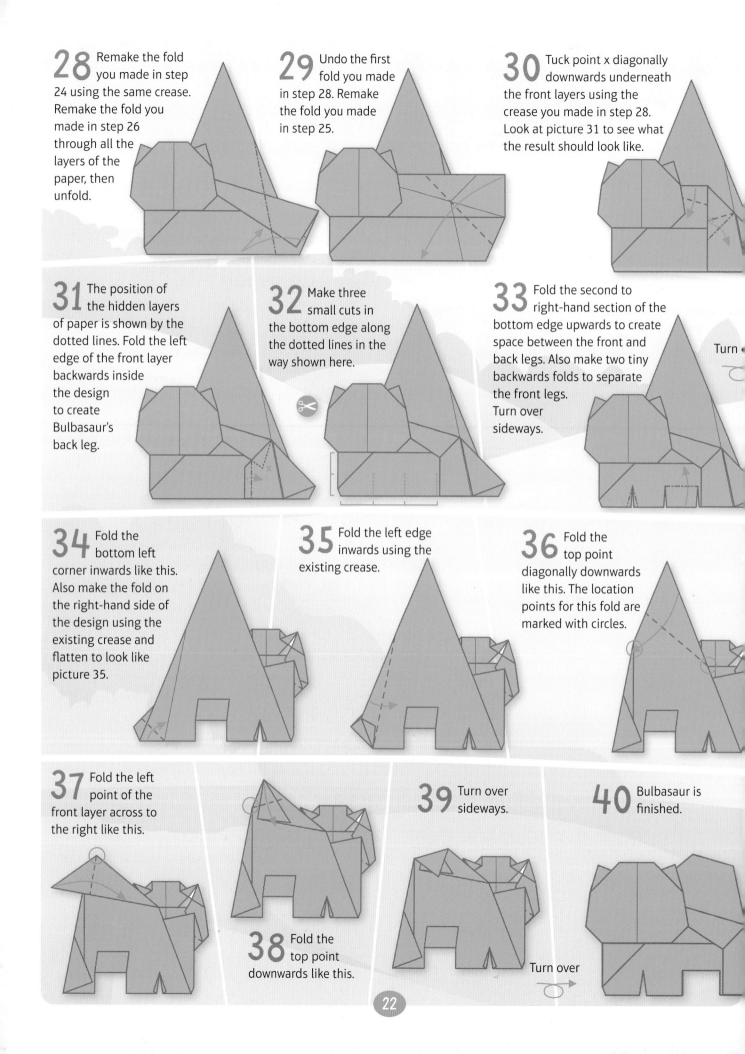

Mudkip

Small but mighty is the phrase for little Mudkip, one of the most loved Pokémon of the Hoenn region. It's got crazy fins and orange cheek gills, and as an amphibious Pokémon it's no surprise that it loves swamps and marshes. You can fold your own Mudkip by following the simple instructions overleaf.

TYPE: Water **HEIGHT:** 0.4 m/1'04" **WEIGHT:** 7.6 kg/16.8 lbs

How To Make
Mudkip

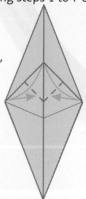

Mudkip is folded from two sheets of paper – a full-size square, which becomes the head and body, and a quarter-size square, which becomes the tail.

You can find the template for the full-size square on page 59 and for the quarter-size square on page 63.

Folding the head and body

Make sure you start folding the full size square with the white side of the paper facing towards you and with the asterisk at the top. Begin by following steps 1 to 7 of Pikachu on page 5.

8 Fold both front flaps in half outwards, then unfold.

9 Fold both outside corners inwards so that the lower part of the top sloping edges end up lying on the creases you made in step 8. Try to make sure your folds are as symmetrical as possible.

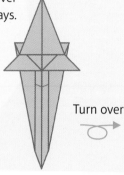

10 Remake the folds you made in step 8.

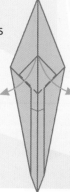

11 Fold the top point downwards like this.

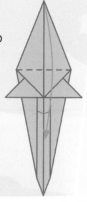

12 Fold the front point upwards like this.

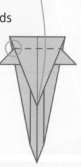

13 Turn over sideways.

Turn over

14 Fold the bottom point upwards. Look at picture 15 to see what the result should look like.

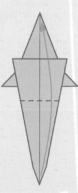

15 Turn over sideways.

Turn over

16 Fold the bottom edge upwards like this. Allow the hidden layers to swivel into view as you do this. The next picture shows what the result should look like.

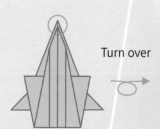

17 Insert one point of a pair of scissors inside the layers as shown here and cut through all the front layers along the fold marked by the dotted line.

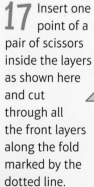

18 Pull the layers released by the cut out to the right.

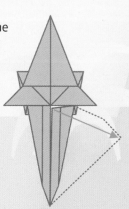

19 Fold the right point inwards. The location points for this fold are marked with circles.

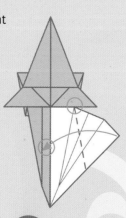

20 Fold the bottom point to the centre of the bottom edge of the top front layers.

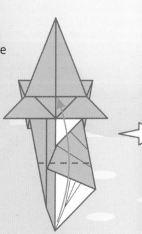

21 Fold the left corner of the bottom front layer inwards like this. The location points for this fold are marked with circles. Also fold both bottom corners of the top front layers upwards as shown.

22 Swivel the bottom front layer out of sight by reversing the direction of the crease you made in step 21. Also undo the two creases you made in the bottom corners of the top front layers.

23 Fold the right edge of the bottom front layers onto the bottom edge, allowing the hidden layer to swivel into view. Also turn the bottom corners of the top front layers inside out between the layers using the creases you made in step 21.

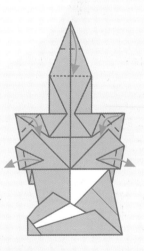

24 Fold the tip of the left point of the bottom front layers inwards to blunt the point. Also fold the outside edges of the top front layers inwards as shown. Fold the tips of the middle front layers inwards as well. Try to make sure that your design remains symmetrical. Picture 25 shows you what the result should look like.

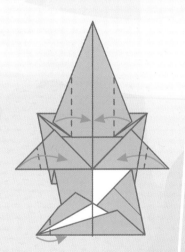

25 Fold the top point downwards like this. Also fold the tips of the middle front layers outwards as shown and fold the top left and right corners inwards to round the face.

26 Your design should now look like this. Turn over sideways.

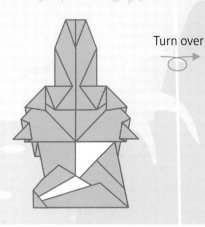

Turn over

27 Finish Mudkip's head and body by folding these two corners backwards out of sight.

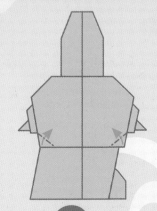

28 Mudkip's head and body are finished.

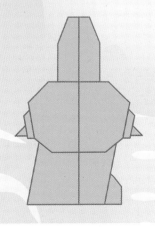

Folding the tail

Make sure you start folding the quarter size square with the white side of the paper facing towards you and with the asterisk at the top.

29 Fold in half sideways, then unfold.

30 Fold the right edge onto the crease you made in step 29.

31 Fold in half downwards.

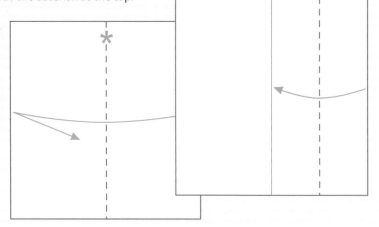

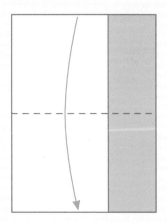

32 Fold the top left corner inwards. You do not need to be completely accurate with this fold.

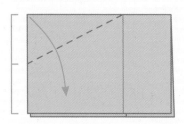

33 Fold the bottom left corner inwards as well.

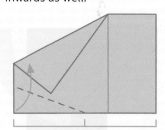

34 Now fold the top right corner inwards. There are no location points for this fold. Just try to make it look as much like picture 35 as you can.

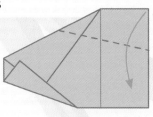

35 Fold the bottom right corner inwards as well.

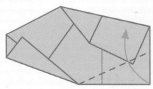

36 And finally fold the bottom point upwards a little.

37 Mudkip's tail is finished.

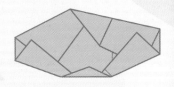

Putting Mudkip together

38 Apply glue to the area marked with a circle and attach Mudkip's tail as shown.

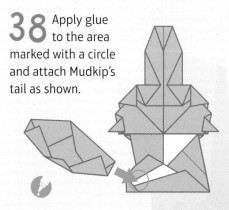

39 Turn over sideways.

40 Mudkip is finished.

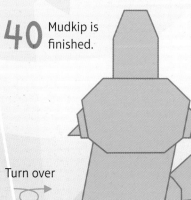

Turn over

26

Gengar

Just how scary can origami be? Gengar intends to find out! This ghostly Shadow Pokémon has a mouth full of teeth and some small claws, and it loves to find ways to scare the unwary. Fold a little haunting into your Gengar!

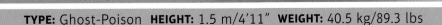

TYPE: Ghost-Poison **HEIGHT:** 1.5 m/4'11" **WEIGHT:** 40.5 kg/89.3 lbs

How To Make
Gengar

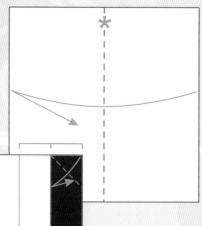

Gengar is folded from eight sheets of paper – one full-size square, which becomes the head and body, and seven quarter-size squares, which become the arms, legs, spikes and tail.

You can find the template for the full-size square on page 61 and for the quarter-size squares on pages 63 and 65.

Folding the head and body

Make sure you start folding the full-size square with the white side of the paper facing towards you and with the asterisk at the top.

1 Fold in half sideways, then unfold.

2 Fold the right edge inwards like this. Picture 3 shows what the result should look like. When you have finished making this fold the right half of the paper should be half coloured and half white. The top and bottom edges must also line up neatly.

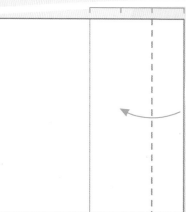

3 Fold the top right corner inwards like this, then unfold.

4 Fold the top edge downwards like this. The circle shows you how to locate this fold.

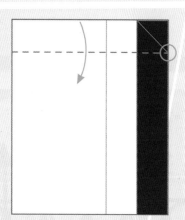

5 Make sure all the left and right edges line up. Fold the top left corner inwards like this, then unfold.

6 Now fold the left-hand edge inwards as well. The circle shows you how to locate this fold.

7 Make sure all the top and bottom edges line up. If you have folded accurately the left half of the paper should be half coloured and half white. Pull out the top and right-hand layers and flatten the paper to look like picture 8.

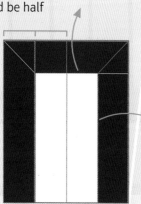

8 Fold the top left corner inwards using the existing crease, then unfold.

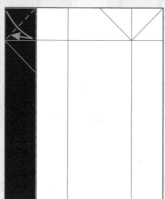

9 Unfold the left-hand side.

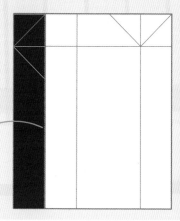

10 Fold the top edge downwards using the crease you made in step 4.

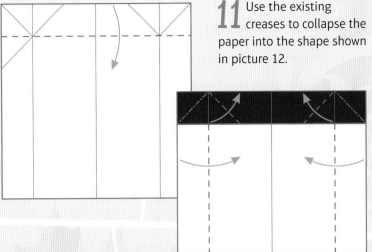

11 Use the existing creases to collapse the paper into the shape shown in picture 12.

12 Fold the bottom edge onto the top edge of the back layers, then unfold.

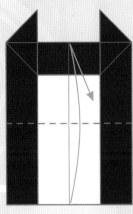

13 Fold the bottom edge onto the crease you made in step 12.

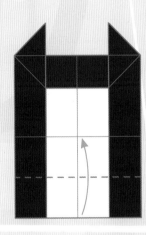

14 Fold both the right and left top corners inwards like this.

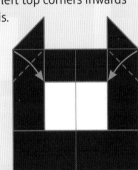

15 Fold the central points of both front layers outwards to create Gengar's ears.

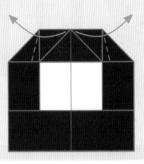

16 Fold both the left and right edges inwards. The circles show you how to locate these folds.

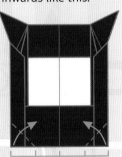

17 Fold both the bottom corners inwards like this.

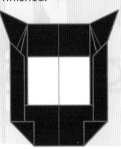

18 Gengar's head and body are finished.

Folding the arms and legs

You need to fold two arms and two legs, all of which are identical. Make sure you start folding all the quarter size squares with the white side of the paper facing towards you.

19 Fold in half sideways, then unfold.

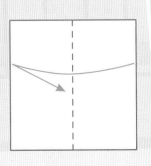

20 Fold both outside edges into the centre.

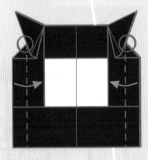

21 Fold both the front layers in half outwards, then unfold.

22 Fold the top right corner inwards like this. Note that the crease starts at the centre of the top edge and that the corner ends up touching the left-hand quarter crease.

23 Fold the top left corner inwards as well so that the top edge ends up on top of the right-hand sloping edge.

24 Fold the right corner of the front layer outwards so that the result looks like picture 25. The circle is there to show you that the bottom of the crease starts approximately half way between the left edge and the left quarter way crease.

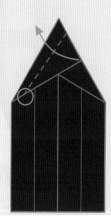

25 Bring the middle layers (marked with a circle) to the front.

26 Repeat fold 24 on the new front flap.

27 Fold both outside edges inwards to the quarter way creases.

28 The first arm (or leg) is finished. Fold three more.

Folding the tail

Make sure you start folding the quarter size square with the white side of the paper facing towards you.

29 Fold in half diagonally.

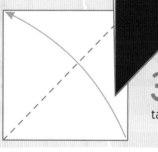

30 That's it! Gengar's tail is finished!

Folding the spikes

You need to fold two sets of spikes, both of which are identical. Make sure you start folding all the quarter size squares with the white side of the paper facing towards you.

31 Fold in half diagonally.

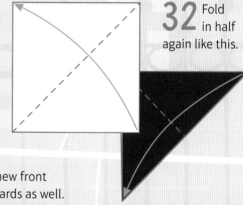

32 Fold in half again like this.

33 Fold the front layer upwards. There are no location points for this fold. Just try to make it look as much like picture 34 as possible.

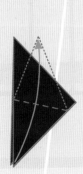

34 Turn over sideways.

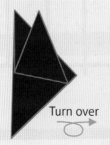

Turn over

35 Fold the new front layer upwards as well. There are no location points for this fold. Just try to make it look as much like picture 36 as possible.

36 This is the first set of spikes. You will need to fold two.

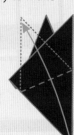

Putting Gengar together

37 Begin by gluing the arms in place like this. They should touch in the middle of Gengar's back and cross the sides of its body more or less centrally.

38 Glue the legs on like this. The legs also touch in the middle of the back. The outside edges of the legs go through the points where the sides of its body change direction at the bottom (all marked with circles).

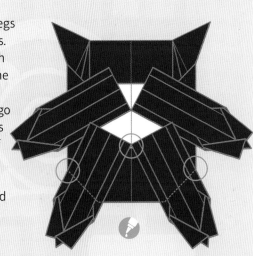

39 Glue the first set of spikes in position like this.

40 Glue the second set of spikes like this.

41 Now all you need to do is glue the tail on as well and turn Gengar over sideways.

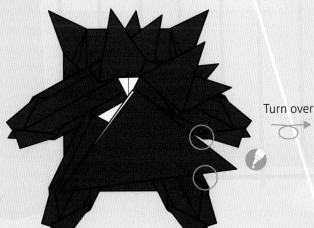

Turn over

42 Gengar is finished.

Snivy

You might think that a Grass Snake Pokémon would be tough to fold, with all those curves, but Snivy has enough edges and points to make a wonderful origami Pokémon! Add in that lively green and a big eye, and you'll soon see that the Grass-type Pokémon makes a pretty great paper-type Pokémon too!

TYPE: Grass **HEIGHT:** 0.6 m/2'00" **WEIGHT:** 8.1 kg/17.9 lbs

How To Make
Snivy

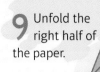

Snivy is folded from two sheets of paper, a full-size square which becomes the head and body, and a small triangle, which becomes the tail. You can find the template for the full-size square on page 67 and the small triangle on page 71.

Folding the head and body

Make sure you start folding the full-size square with the white side of the paper facing towards you and with the asterisk at the top. Begin by following steps 1 to 7 of Pikachu on page 5.

8 Fold both front flaps downwards. Lift the left flap upwards again.

9 Unfold the right half of the paper.

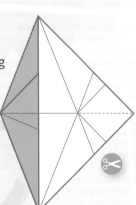

10 Cut along the dotted line.

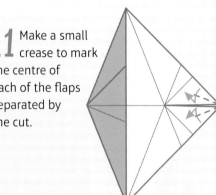

11 Make a small crease to mark the centre of each of the flaps separated by the cut.

12 Remake the folds you undid in step 9 so that the design looks like picture 13.

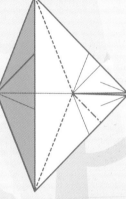

13 Turn over sideways.

14 Fold in half sideways from right to left.

Turn over

15 Fold the front flap in half downwards like this.

16 Fold the top left edge inwards to butt against the top edge of the front layers.

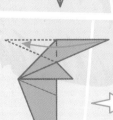

17 Fold the top right point across to the left as shown.

18 Pull out the middle layers at the top of the design and flatten to look like picture 19.

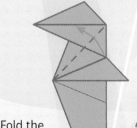

19 Fold the lower edge of the top front layers diagonally upwards as shown.

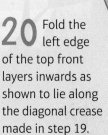

20 Fold the left edge of the top front layers inwards as shown to lie along the diagonal crease made in step 19.

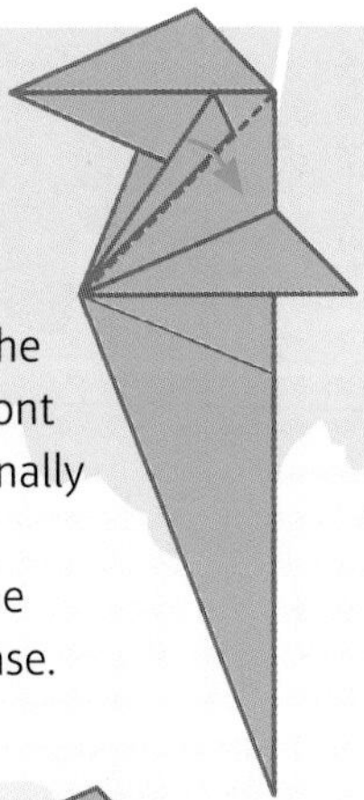

21 Fold the top front layers diagonally inwards like this using the existing crease.

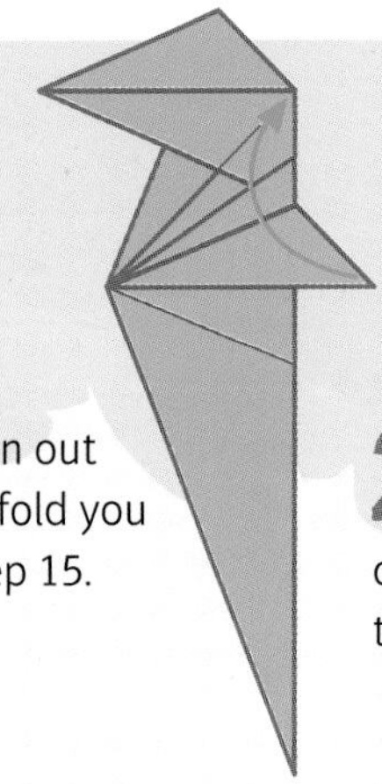

22 Open out the fold you made in step 15.

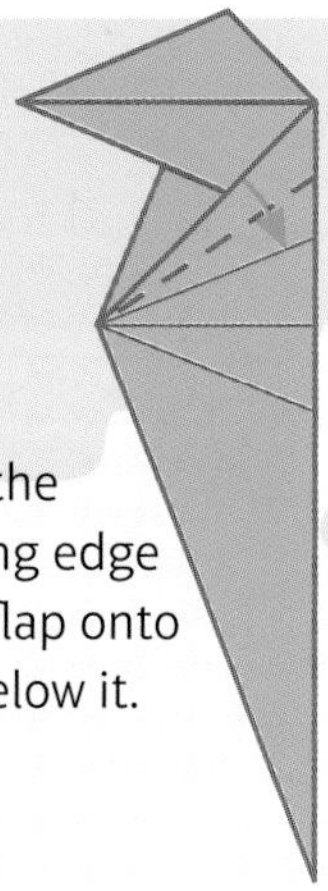

23 Fold the sloping edge of the front flap onto the crease below it.

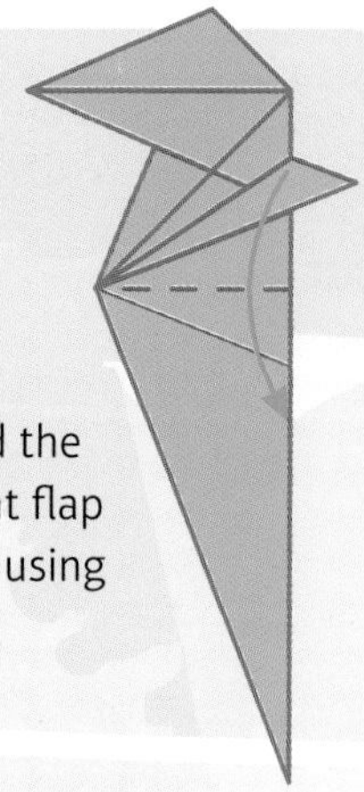

24 Fold the front flap downwards using the existing crease.

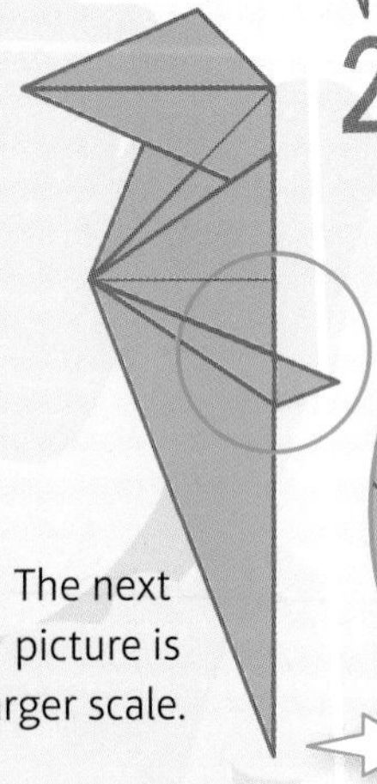

25 The next picture is on a larger scale.

26 Fold the point in half upwards like this.

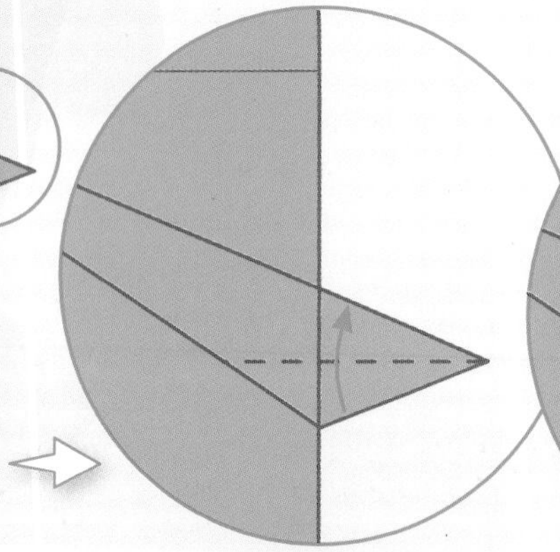

27 Fold the tip of the point upwards in between the layers as shown.

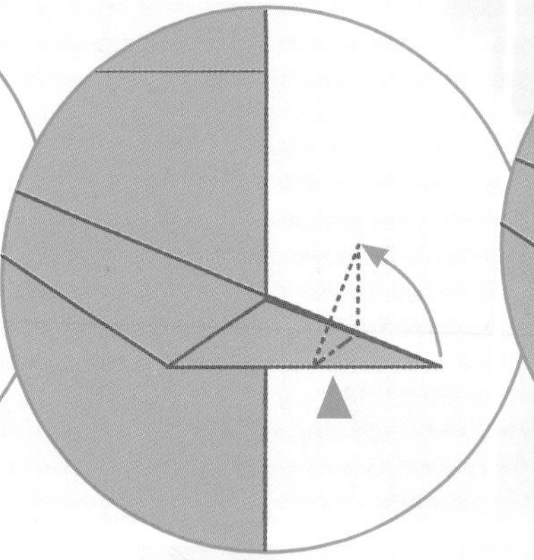

28 The result should look like this.

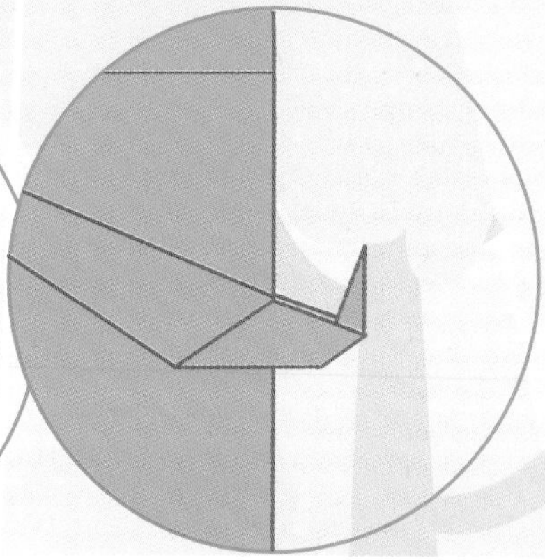

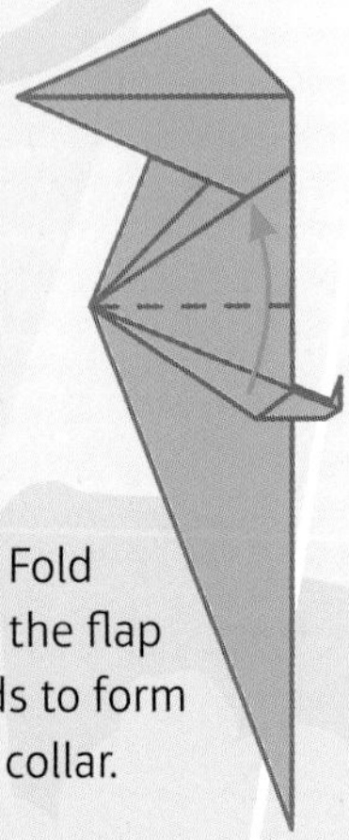

29 Fold the flap upwards to form Snivy's collar.

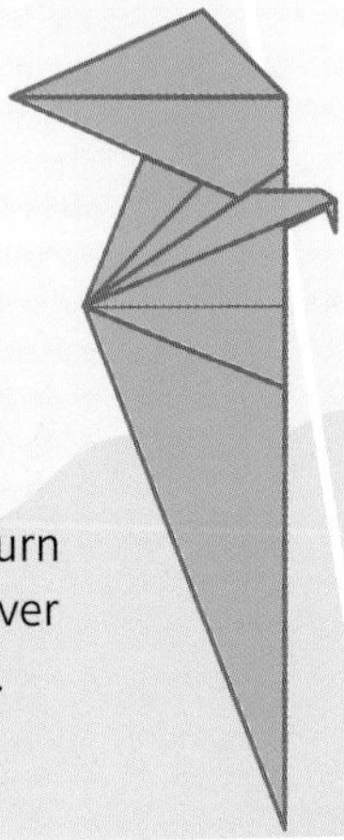

30 Turn over sideways.

31 Fold just the front layer upwards using the existing crease.

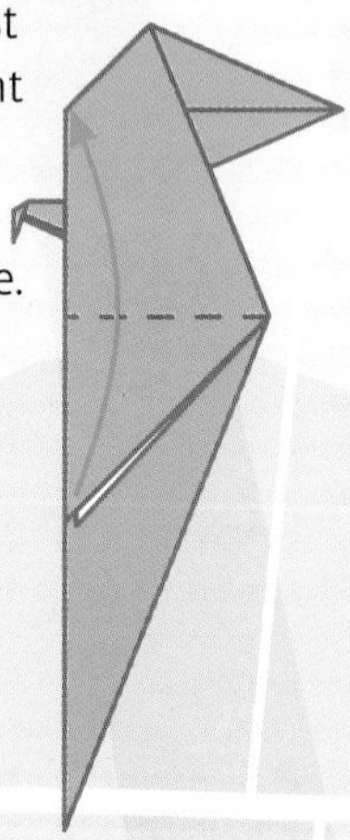

Turn over

32 Fold the bottom point upwards and to the left like this. Also fold the top right point across to the left, making sure the line of the fold is vertical.

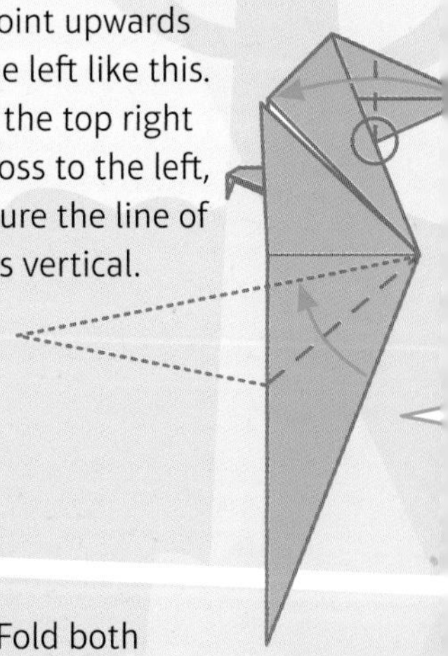

33 Fold the top front layer back out to the right to create Snivy's beak. Also fold the middle front flap downwards using the existing crease.

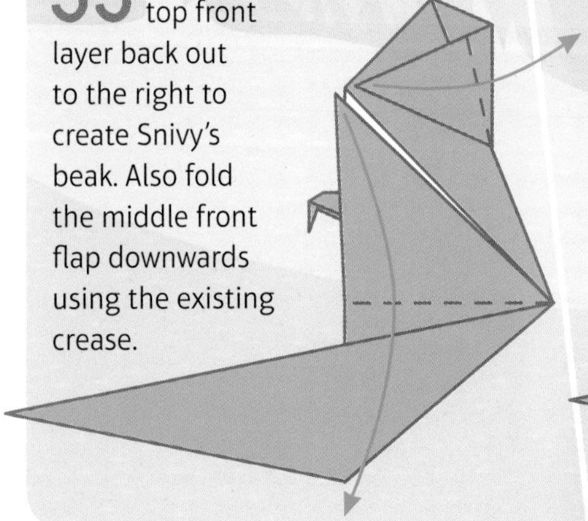

34 Fold both white triangular flaps in half like this, then unfold.

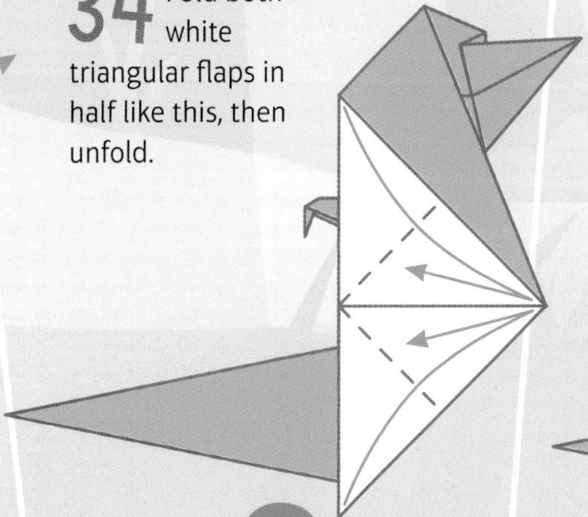

35 Fold both white triangular flaps in half again like this, then unfold.

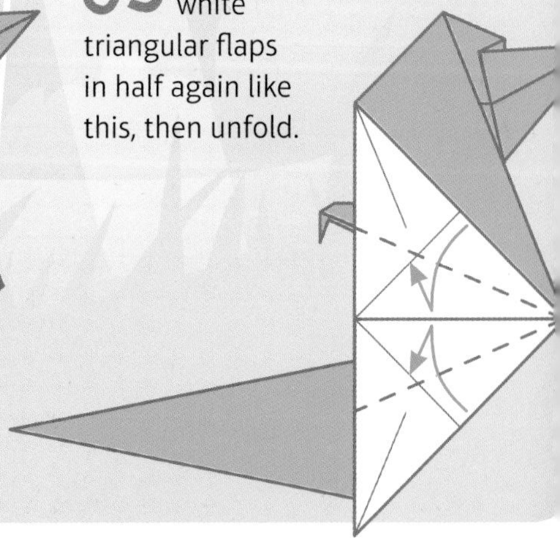

36 Fold the right edge of the bottom white triangular flap onto the crease you made in step 34, then unfold.

37 Fold the sloping edge of the bottom white triangular flap into the crease you made in step 35, then unfold.

38 Use the creases you have made in the last two steps, and one of the creases made in step 11 to collapse this flap to look like picture 39.

39 Fold the top of the leg upwards and to the right to create a foot. Also repeat steps 36 to 38 on the top white triangular flap, but leave gaps between the edges of the paper and the creases made in steps 34 and 35 when you make folds 36 and 37. The result of this will be that the two legs will not lay exactly on top of each other after you carry out step 38.

40 Fold the top front layer downwards using the existing crease.

41 Repeat step 39 on the second leg to create a second foot. Also fold the left point upwards and inwards as shown to begin to create Snivy's tail.

42 Fold the bottom point upwards like this. Also thin the body by folding the right edge of the front layers inwards like this and flattening them to look like picture 43.

43 Note that there should be a dip between the top of the head and the beak. Turn over sideways.

Turn over

44 Snivy's head and body are finished.

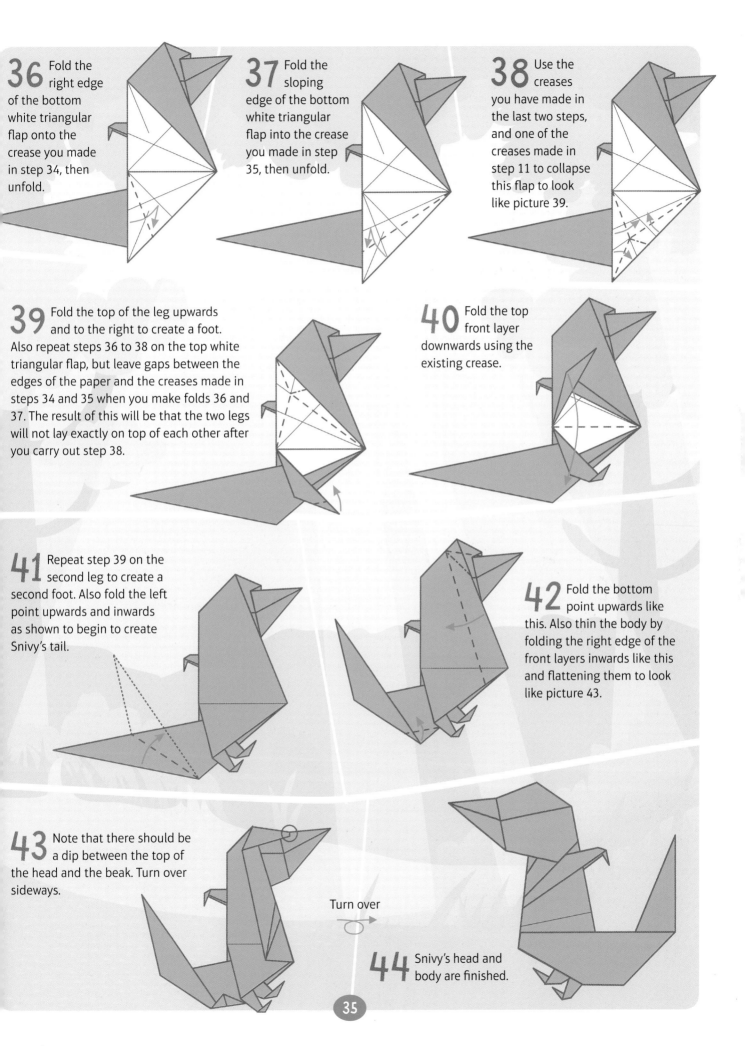

Folding the tail

Make sure you start folding the triangle with the white side of the paper facing towards you and with the asterisk at the bottom.

45 Fold the sloping right edge inwards as shown. You are trying to divide the angle at the bottom exactly into thirds.

46 Fold the sloping left edge inwards as well. Adjust your folds until both outside edges line up neatly.

47 Swing the front flap to the back.

48 Fold the bottom point upwards so that the design looks like picture 49.

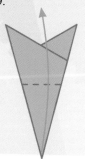

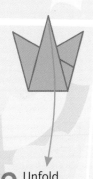

49 Unfold.

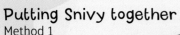

50 Fold the bottom point upwards in between the other layers by reversing the crease made in step 48.

51 Turn over sideways.

52 Fold both bottom corners inwards like this, making sure to leave a gap between the creases at the bottom.

53 There is a small pocket at the bottom into which the point of Snivy's existing tail will fit.

Putting Snivy together
Method 1

54 You can fit the tail simply by sliding the right point up inside the pocket in the bottom of the tail like this.

55 Snivy is finished.

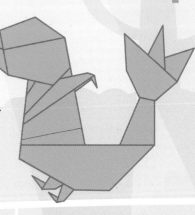

Putting Snivy together
Method 2

54 Alternatively you can use a little glue applied to the back of the design to secure Snivy's tail in place.

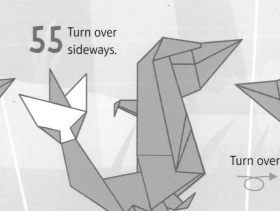

55 Turn over sideways.

56 Snivy is finished.

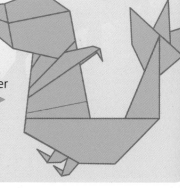

Turn over

Eevee

Eevee is one of those Pokémon that will surprise you, starting simple but able to take on a huge range of shapes and styles, depending on how it evolves. Quite a bit like a simple sheet of paper that folds into hundreds of shapes!

TYPE: Normal **HEIGHT:** 0.3 m/1'00" **WEIGHT:** 6.5 kg/14.3 lbs

How To Make
Eevee

Eevee is folded from two sheets of paper – a full-size square, which becomes the body, head and legs, and a quarter-size square, which becomes the tail.

You can find the template for the full-size square on page 69 and for the quarter-size square on page 71.

Folding the body, head and legs

Make sure you start folding the full-size square with the white side of the paper facing towards you and with the asterisk at the top.

1 Fold in half sideways, then unfold.

2 Fold in half downwards.

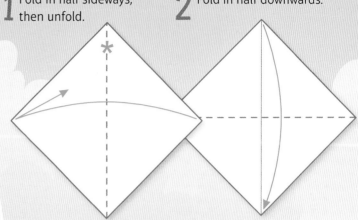

3 Fold the left-hand sloping edge onto the vertical crease.

4 Unfold just the front layer and flatten to look like picture 5.

5 Turn over sideways.

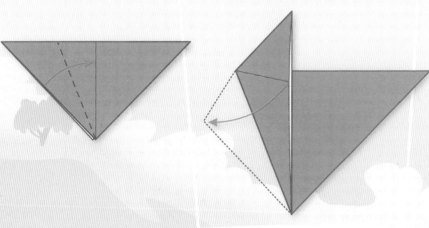

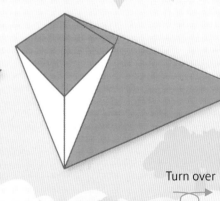

Turn over

6 Fold the sloping top edge onto the vertical crease.

7 Unfold.

8 Fold the top layer across to the right as shown and flatten symmetrically to look like picture 9.

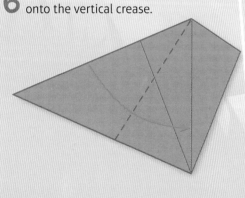

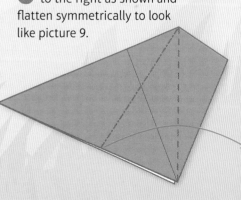

9 Fold both the outside edges inwards to lie on the vertical crease.

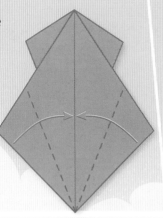

10 Fold the top point downwards to create a horizontal crease between the two outside front corners as shown, then unfold.

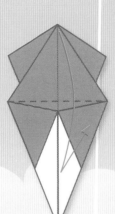

11 Open out the folds made in step 9.

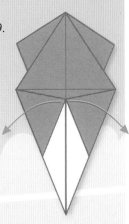

12 Fold the bottom point upwards using the crease made in step 10 and flatten to look like picture 13.

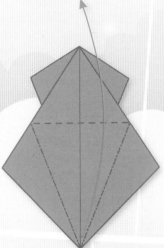

13 Turn over sideways.

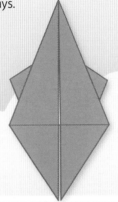

14 Fold the outside edges of the front layers onto the vertical crease as shown.

Turn over

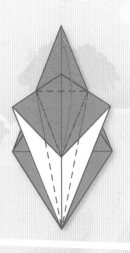

15 Fold the top point of the front layers downwards as shown, then unfold.

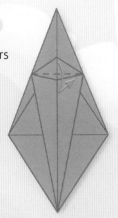

16 Open out the folds made in step 14.

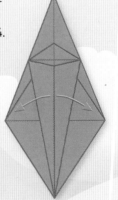

17 Fold the bottom point of the front layer upwards using the crease made in step 15 and flatten to look like picture 18. Two new creases will form as you flatten the paper.

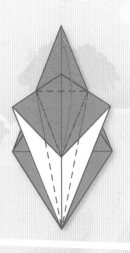

18 Fold the top point down to the bottom, crease, then unfold. This fold is only made in the front layers of the paper.

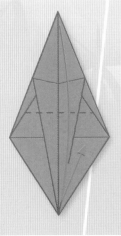

19 Make two small creases between the points marked with circles and use them to open out the front layers. Flatten the layers to look like picture 20.

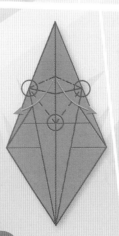

20 Fold the top point of the front layers downwards using the crease made in step 18.

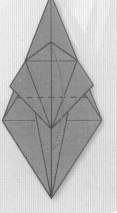

21 Fold the bottom point of the front layers upwards so that the crease made in step 17 lies along the top edge.

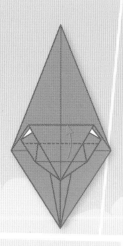

22 Pull the flap marked with a circle downwards and flatten so that the design looks like picture 23.

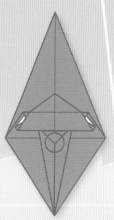

23 Fold the top left edge of the front flap downwards to lie along the bottom edge.

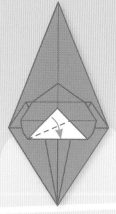

24 Do the same to the top right edge.

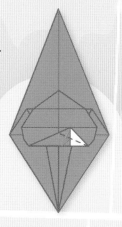

25 Fold the front flap downwards like this.

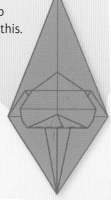

26 Turn over sideways.

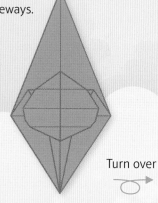

Turn over

27 Fold both outside corners into the centre like this.

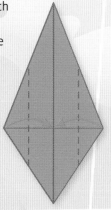

28 Begin to form the feet by folding the bottom point of the right-hand half of the paper onto the point marked with a circle.

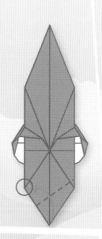

29 Now fold the tip of the front point back to the right to form the first foot. The sole of the foot should be horizontal when you have done this.

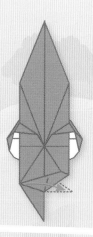

30 Repeat steps 28 amd 29 on the left-hand half of the paper. You will need to temporarily undo folds 28 and 29 to achieve this.

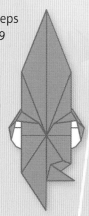

31 Adjust your folds, if necessary, so that the bottom edges of both feet form a straight line. Turn over sideways.

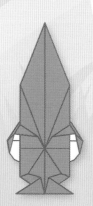

Turn over

32 Fold the top of the front layers backwards into the pocket behind it using the existing crease.

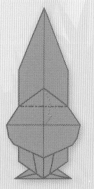

33 Fold the top point downwards like this.

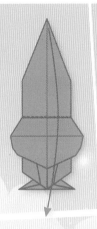

34 Fold the bottom point upwards again so that the crease forms as nearly as possible in the position shown.

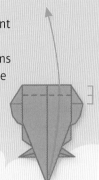

35 Turn the bottom corners of the front layers inside out to begin to shape the head. Also pull the loose front layers of the feet out downwards.

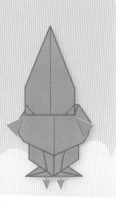

36 Fold the bottom of the feet backwards out of sight. If you want to be really neat, tuck them into the pockets behind them.

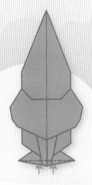

37 Turn over sideways.

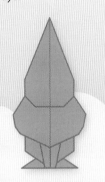

Turn over

38 Fold the top point downwards as shown. Look at picture 39 to see what the result should look like.

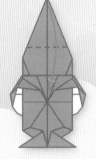

39 Cut along the dotted line to separate the ears. Also fold the points of the feet inwards to blunt the toes.

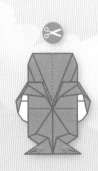

40 Fold the ears upwards like this.

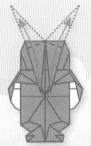

41 Eevee is finished apart from its tail.

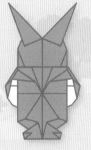

Folding the tail

Make sure you start folding the quarter-size square with the white side of the paper facing towards you and with the asterisk at the top.

42 Fold in half downwards, then unfold.

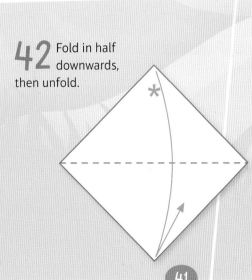

43 Fold both right-hand sloping edges onto the horizontal crease.

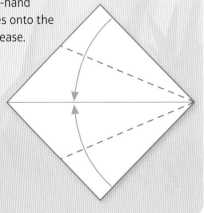

44 Do the same thing to the left-hand sloping edges.

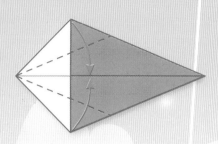

45 Fold the bottom right-hand edge inwards so that it passes through the top point (see picture 46).

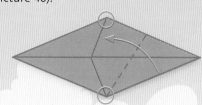

46 Unfold.

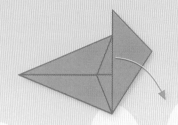

47 Fold the bottom right-hand edge inwards again so that it lies on the crease made in step 45.

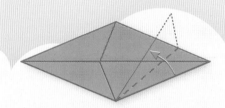

48 Fold the right point inwards so that it ends up lying on the top edge.

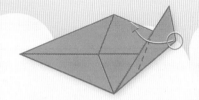

49 Fold the bottom point inwards like this to finish shaping the tail. There is no location point to help you here. You just have to do it by eye.

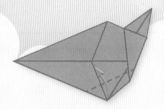

Attaching the tail

50 You can either glue or tape Eevee's tail in place or follow steps 51 to 54, which alter the tail so that it will lock into place by itself. The choice is yours.

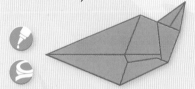

51 Fold the right point back along the top edge like this.

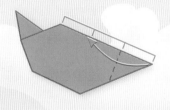

Turn over

52 Turn over sideways.

Turn over

53 You can attach the tail by inserting the tab you created in step 51 into this pocket...

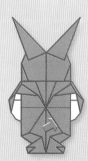

54 ...like this. Turn over sideways.

Turn over

55 Fold the two halves of the design slightly backwards along the line of the vertical crease. Eevee is finished.

Charizard

Charizard is a fan favourite Pokémon, and – let's be honest – it's one of the more difficult origami Pokémon, with wings and claws, and a smaller head. Origami Charizard is like a Gym Battle – be sure you're ready for it before you dive in!

TYPE: Fire-Flying   **HEIGHT:** 1.7 m/5'07"   **WEIGHT:** 90.5 kg/199.5 lbs

How To Make
Charizard

Charizard is folded from five sheets of paper – two full-size squares, which become the body, head and tail, and three triangles, which become the wings and the legs.

You can find the template for the full-size squares on pages 73 and 75 and for the triangles on pages 77 and 79.

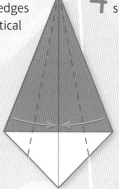

Folding the head and body

Make sure you start folding the full-size square with the white side of the paper facing towards you and with the asterisk at the top.

1 Fold in half sideways, then unfold.

2 Fold both top sloping edges onto the vertical crease.

3 Fold both top sloping edges onto the vertical crease.

4 Turn over sideways.

Turn over

5 Fold in half downwards.

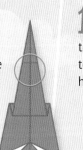

6 Turn over sideways.

7 Fold the top edge downwards, allowing the hidden layers to flip forward as you make the fold.

Turn over

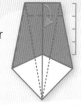

8 Fold the top point downwards like this. Also fold the bottom point upwards as shown.

9 Fold both bottom corners inwards slightly to shape the body. Follow the circled steps to make the horn.

10 Carefully cut along the dotted line to create the horn.

11 The result should look like this.

12 Fold the top point downwards using the crease made in step 8 and allowing the horn to flip upwards.

13 Turn over sideways.

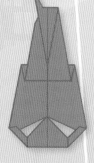

14 Fold the top left corner inwards, allowing the head to flip into the position shown in step 15.

Turn over

15 Turn over sideways.

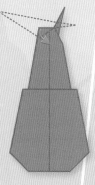

Turn over

44

16 Narrow the neck by folding both sides inwards like this. Flatten the folds so that the result looks like picture 17.

17 Note how the paper flattens at the base of the neck. Follow the circled steps to make the snout.

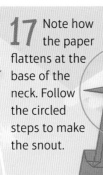

18 Fold the point of the head inwards like this.

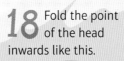

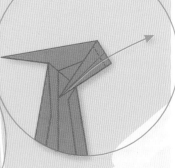

19 Fold the front point to the right to form the snout.

20 Fold the tip of the top right point inwards to blunt the snout.

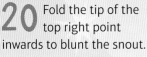

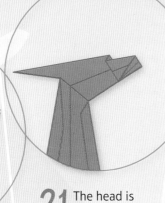

21 The head is finished.

22 Fold both top corners of the body inwards to round the shoulders.

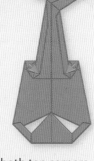

23 Charizard's head and body are finished.

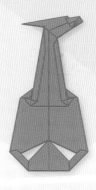

Folding the legs

Make sure you start folding the triangle with the decorated side of the paper facing towards you and with the asterisk at the top. The asterisk is printed on the white side of the paper.

24 Fold in half sideways, then unfold.

25 Fold the left edge onto the vertical crease.

26 Fold the right edge of the front layer onto the left edge.

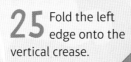

27 Repeat steps 25 and 26 on the right-hand half of the paper.

28 Turn over sideways.

Turn over

29 Fold both outside corners of the front layers inwards like this.

30 Unfold.

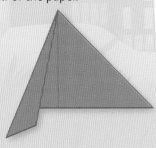

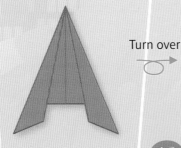

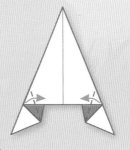

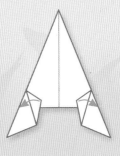

31 Fold the bottom edge of the front layer upwards like this so that the paper flattens to look like picture 32.

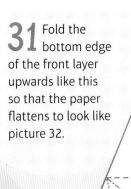

32 Fold the top point downwards so that the point ends up behind the front layer. Also fold the tops of both bottom points inwards as shown.

33 Turn over sideways.

34 Charizard's legs are finished.

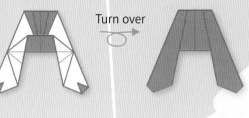

Turn over

Folding the wings

Make sure you start folding the correct triangle (the right wing is folded first) with the decorated side of the paper facing towards you and with the asterisk at the top. The asterisk is printed on the white side of the paper.

35 Begin by folding the right sloping edge onto the bottom edge to create a short crease between them. You will need this crease in step 41.

36 Follow steps 25 and 26 so that your paper looks like picture 37.

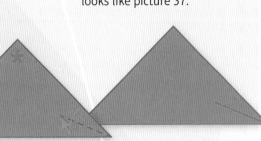

37 Fold the right sloping edge to butt against the right edge of the front layers, then unfold. Also fold the bottom corner inwards as shown.

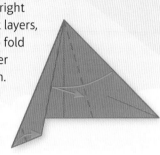

38 Turn over sideways.

39 Fold the left sloping edge onto the right edge.

Turn over

40 Fold the front layer to the left using the crease made in step 37.

41 Fold the bottom edge of the front layer onto the crease you made in step 35 and flatten to look like picture 42.

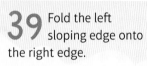

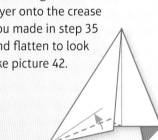

42 Fold the top point downwards like this, then unfold.

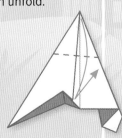

43 Follow the magnified steps to make the claw.

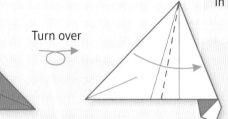

44 Fold the top of the left sloping edge onto the crease you made in step 42, then unfold.

45 Fold the top of the right sloping edge onto the crease you made in step 42, then unfold.

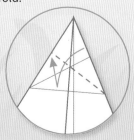

46 Fold the top of the right sloping edge onto the crease you made in step 45.

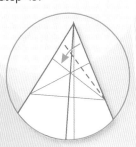

47 Fold the left point of the front flap across to the right and flatten so that the top of the left sloping edge of the layer behind folds onto the crease you made in step 44.

48 The result should look like this.

49 The finished wing should look like this.

50 Now make the left wing. This is made in exactly the same way except it is a mirror image of the first one. Charizard's wings are finished.

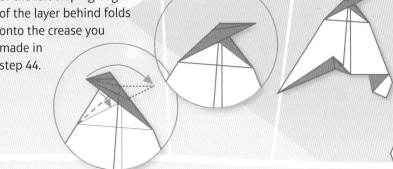

Folding the tail

Begin by following steps 1 to 3 on page 44 of "Folding the head and body."

51 Open out the folds made in step 3.

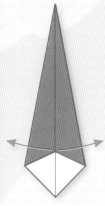

52 Fold the top point downwards like this, then unfold.

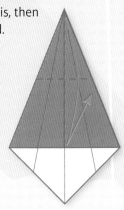

53 Fold the top point downwards onto the crease made in step 52, then unfold.

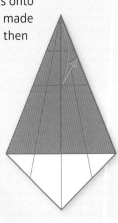

54 Carefully make two tiny cuts along the dotted lines to partially separate the flame from the tail. Look at picture 55 to see what the result should look like. Also fold both bottom sloping edges onto the vertical crease.

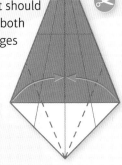

55 Fold both top sloping edges (below the cuts) inwards using the existing creases.

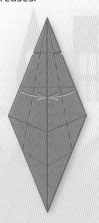

56 Turn over sideways.

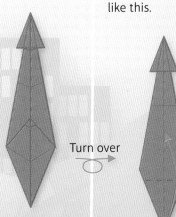

Turn over

57 Fold the bottom point upwards like this.

58 Fold in half backwards using the existing crease.

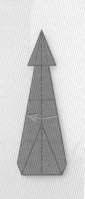

59 Pull the flame vertical then flatten to look like picture 60.

60 Charizard's tail is finished.

Putting Charizard together

61 This is Charizard's right wing. Note the position of the small flap at the back marked with the dotted line.

62 Apply glue to Charizard's body in the position marked with a circle then slide the small flap behind the wing inside the layers at the position indicated by the arrow.

63 This is the result. Add the left wing in exactly the same way.

64 Turn over sideways.

Turn over

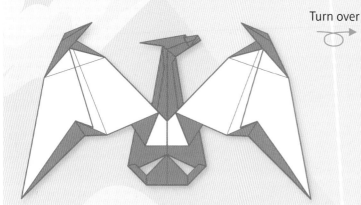

65 Apply glue to the legs at the point marked with a circle and slide them up behind the body until Charizard looks like picture 66.

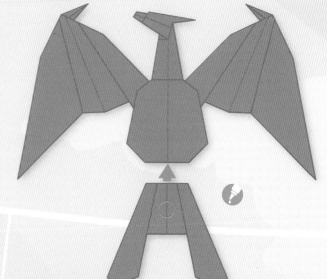

66 Make sure the legs and body are aligned at the position marked by the two upper circles. Apply glue to the tail (at the position marked by the lower circle) and slide it up behind the legs to the position shown in step 67.

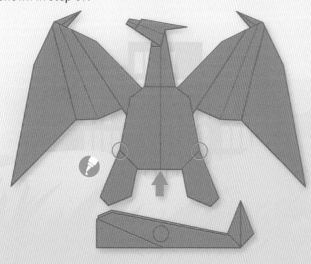

67 Make sure the flame does not touch the wing. Charizard is finished.

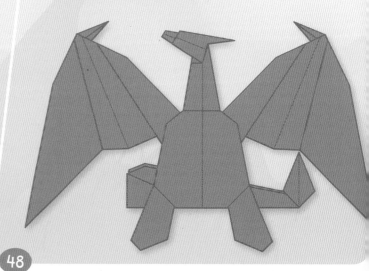

Munchlax

Munchlax is folded from a single square of paper.
See instructions on page 8

*

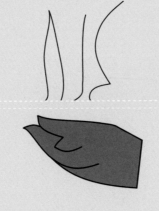

Scraggy

Scraggy is folded from three pieces of paper.
See instructions on page 15

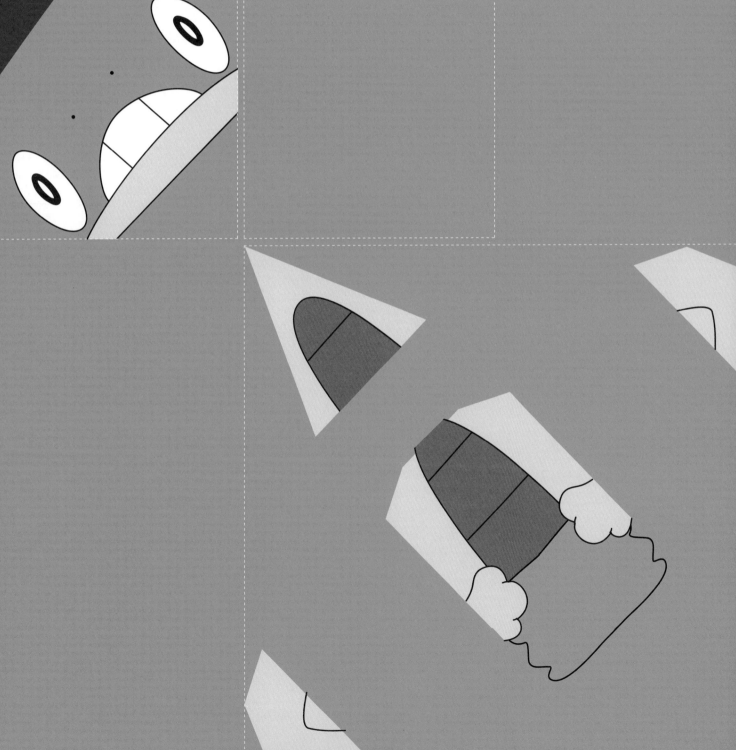

Bulbasaur

Bulbasaur is folded from a single square of paper.
See instructions on page 19

*

Mudkip

Mudkip is folded from two pieces of paper.
You'll find the square for the tail on page 63.
See instructions on page 23

*

The purple squares are for Gengar's arms, legs, spikes or tail. All the pieces are the same size.
See instructions on page 27

The blue square is Mudkip's tail.
See instructions on page 23

*

These squares are for Gengar's arms, legs, spikes or tail. All the pieces are the same size.
See instructions on page 27

Snivy

Snivy is folded from two pieces of paper.
You'll find the triangle for the tail on page 71.
See instructions on page 32

*

The brown square is for Eevee's tail.
See instructions on page 37

The green triangle is for Snivy's tail.
See instructions on page 32